PRAIRIE PLANTS
of ILLINOIS

D1246204

By John W. Voigt
Department of Botany, Southern Illinois University
and
Robert H. Mohlenbrock
Chairman, Department of Botany
Southern Illinois University

Illustrations by Miriam Wysong Meyer
Front and back cover credit Illinois State Museum
In cooperation with the Illinois Department of Conservation
Division of Forestry
R #5
Springfield, Illinois 62707

Printed by authority of the State of Illinois
Issued by
DEPARTMENT OF CONSERVATION
Division of Forestry

TABLE OF CONTENTS

Acknowledgments

The authors are indebted to Dr. David Kenney, Director of the Illinois Department of Conservation, to Mr. Allan Mickelson, State Forester, and to staff foresters Ernest Kunze, Dick Thom and John Sester for their willingness to let us write about the prairie plants of Illinois. Thanks are also given to all our colleagues who helped us in any way in the preparation of this book.

We wish to thank Mr. Vernon Sternberg and the Southern Illinois University Press who were kind enough to let us use the following illustrations from the *Illustrated Flora of Illinois* series: *Andropogon gerardii, Bouteloua curtipendula, Hordeum pusillum. Iris shrevei, Juncus tenuis, Juncus torreyi, Panicum capillare, Panicum oligosanthes* var. *scribnerianum, Panicum virgatum, Poa pratensis, Schizachyrium scoparium, Sisyrinchium angustifolium, Sorghastrum nutans, Spartina pectinata, Sporobolus asper, Sporobolus cryptandrus, Sporobolus heterolepis,* and *Tripsacum dactyloides.*

We are grateful to Mr. Paul Nelson who did the illustration of *Salix humilis* and to Mr. Dan Malkovich and *Illinois Magazine* who let us use some material from that publication.

Thanks are also given to Mrs. Beverly Mohlenbrock who typed the manuscript.

Introduction

This book is designed to provide a better understanding of the prairie plants which comprise a rich vegetational heritage in Illinois.

French explorers and trappers, upon viewing the extensive grasslands of mid-America for the first time, called them "Prairie." Their word had the meaning of a natural meadow. Prairie is a word related to the Latin "pratum", which means meadow.

Prairie is a vegetational community dominated by native grasses. Subordinate to the grasses are many colorful herbs that delight the eye of the traveler and the observer. Interesting patterns are also created by the rippling motion of the grasses under the wind, and shadows by the sun and clouds. The vastness of the land, its rolling topography, motion of the grasses, and changing light and shadows gave the illusion of the ground heaving and swelling and appealed to the same emotions as did the endless oceans.

The prairie was created over a period of thousands of years. Its species became adjusted to the reactions they made upon and among each other and to the extremes of continental climate. The species accommodated each other's needs by differences in stature and in seasonal appearance. The prairie flora became adjusted to grazing by herds of ungulates and to ravaging of wildfire when the plants were dry at maturity. All these factors and others combined to make the prairie a richly integrated community.

In many places the prairie flora will be found to be relatively simple. In Iowa, Shimek, who was an early student of prairie, found the flora to be composed of about 265 species. In Nebraska, on a square mile of prairie, Steiger found 237 species. More than 300 species were indigenous to the prairies of Illinois.

The student of prairie vegetation in Illinois will meet only about ten species of grasses with regularity. These ten species constitute the major dominants (Fig. 1). Several other secondary grass species are encountered much less frequently. About three dozen species of forbs will occur in regularity, and another fifty or more forbs will grow in lesser number and with lessened frequency. The remaining forb species are widely distributed, and even of less frequent occurrence. Some of them are classed as rare. A relatively few

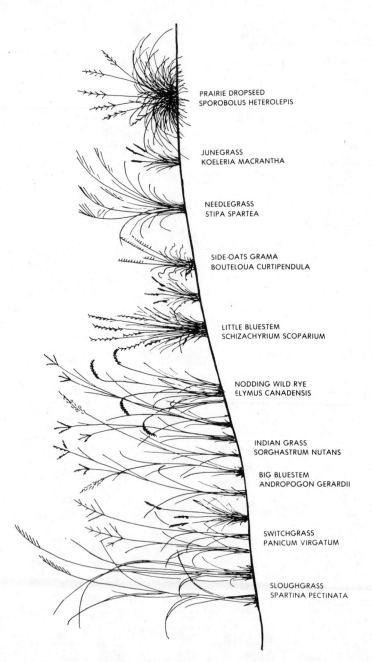

PRAIRIE DROPSEED
SPOROBOLUS HETEROLEPIS

JUNEGRASS
KOELERIA MACRANTHA

NEEDLEGRASS
STIPA SPARTEA

SIDE-OATS GRAMA
BOUTELOUA CURTIPENDULA

LITTLE BLUESTEM
SCHIZACHYRIUM SCOPARIUM

NODDING WILD RYE
ELYMUS CANADENSIS

INDIAN GRASS
SORGHASTRUM NUTANS

BIG BLUESTEM
ANDROPOGON GERARDII

SWITCHGRASS
PANICUM VIRGATUM

SLOUGHGRASS
SPARTINA PECTINATA

FIGURE 1
MAJOR DOMINANTS

species make up most of the vegetation in some prairies, but in others, such as sand prairies, hill prairies, and savannas, many additional species are encountered. By becoming acquainted with about fifty species, including both grasses and forbs, one has made a good beginning in the study of prairie. By increasing the number of familiar species to over one hundred, one feels at home in most prairie situations and has, by this time, learned the more important habitat associations and community relations among the dominants.

Throughout Illinois there were marked differences in the growth of plants. In addition to the obvious factor of climate, there were differences in drainage, soil quality, topography, degree of burning, kinds of animals present, as well as many other factors. When all of these became integrated, they expressed recognizable geographic variations in the appearance of prairie.

The prairies of Illinois were bounded on the east by the deciduous forest. Often there was a transition area of savanna, particularly in northeastern Illinois. Rainfall was an important factor upon the growth and stature of the prairie grasses. Our Illinois prairies were chiefly tall grasses and tall herbs intermingled with grasses and herbs of middle stature. There were, as well, some grasses and herbs of short stature. There is a gradient from short to tall grasses with the shorter plants blooming in the spring and the taller plants blooming in the fall. Our "tall grass prairies" had a three-layered structure; they were called the True Prairie (Fig. 2). True Prairie extended westward to a broad transition area near the 97th Meridian where it gave way to Mixed Prairie. Mixed Prairie was so named because it was a mixture of mid- and short grasses and herbs. The Mixed Prairie extended over 400 miles farther west to the Rocky Mountains, and ranged north from Canada and south to Texas and old Mexico.

Prairies of mid-continental America owe their existence to the geological uplifting of the Rocky Mountains millions of years ago. As a result of the mountain building, the westerly winds were caused to drop their moisture on the west slopes of the Rockies, creating a rain shadow on the east side of the mountains. This increased the dryness and speeded the evolution of the grass life form and of the spread of grassland vegetation over the plains area. Mammals, including a number of grazing types such as horses rhinoceros, and camels, evolved simultaneously and were present in North America in the Eocene epoch when the grasslands were developed.

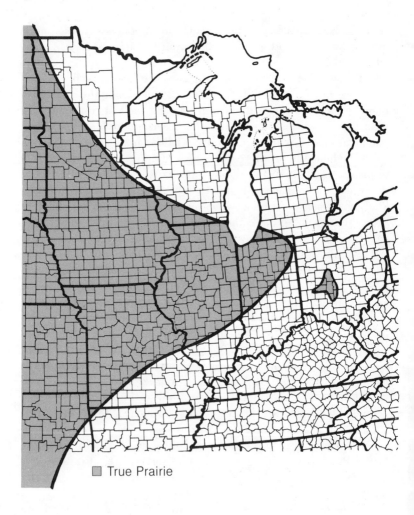

True Prairie

FIGURE 2

About 200,000 years ago, glaciation destroyed most of the vegetation in what is now Illinois. Upon retreat of glacial ice, prairies became established upon the new lands. The deepest penetration of this glaciation was to within 50 or 60 miles of the southern tip of Illinois. A most recent glaciation, the Wisconsinan, occurred about 10,000 years ago, and covered the northeastern third of the state.

Illinois prairies as seen by the early French explorers were largely on the glaciated lands. Most of the present prairie remnants are also on glaciated lands. Exceptions are the small inclusions of prairie within the forests south of the glacial limits or on the bluffs and the driftless areas which escaped glaciation.

Scattered lowland areas developed following continental glaciation. There was a slow migration of prairie onto unglaciated lands. These areas were extensive in eastern and northeastern Illinois and supported wet prairie. There were also lowland areas not quite so wet which were simply lowland prairie. The upland prairies were drier and these were quickly put into agricultural use. The largest part of the great Illinois prairie was either upland or lowland-wet prairie types. Before settlement, about two-thirds of the vegetation in what is now the State of Illinois was native or natural grassland. Illinois became known at an early date as the "Prairie State."

Along the sides of the Rock River Valley of northern Illinois, there are deposits of glacial rock or gravel outwash. Upon these areas there developed a distinctive type of prairie which showed some affinities with the prairies to the West. This kind of prairie, dry because of porous gravel, is known as the Gravel Hill Prairie.

In other places, particularly along the Mississippi and Illinois Rivers, there were deposits of river sand where prairie vegetation developed. The largest of these is in the Illinois River valley in Mason and adjoining counties. These Sand Prairies show a strong affinity to the western prairies in terms of their species composition. At the turn of the century, these prairies were studied by Dr. Henry Allan Gleason, famous American plant ecologist. One of the Nature Preserves in Illinois in Mason County is named in honor of Dr. Gleason, who was a native of Illinois.

As the ice sheet of the continental glacier receded, its melt waters created braided streams which covered broad valleys. This left exposed much fine-textured soil material which upon drying, was blown onto the uplands and deposited as loess. On these loess-covered hills, some prairies developed. The prairies bordering the major rivers were called Loess Hill Prairies.

The early prairie pioneers depended upon the prairie as a source of forage for their livestock. As the prairies were grazed by domestic stock, the vegetation began to change. Some species were more palatable and nutritious. These were constantly sought and grazed, and the plants were weakened and replaced by others. Thus, some plants decreased, some increased, and many introduced species became established as invaders. Over a period of time, the prairie lost its stability because its carrying capacity was exceeded. The original character of the prairie was changed by a replacement of native species by those of outside origin and of a weedy nature.

Native grasses continue to have many uses. They are important in erosion control, forage production, wildlife food and cover, reclamation, roadside planting, and beautification projects. Native grasses and grasslands have provided agricultural soils of unmatched richness. One needs only to look at maps showing the distribution and productivity of cereal grain or of farmland concentration to see the close correspondence the present cultural landscape and economy have with the original range of the bluestem grasses, the prairie chicken, the bison, and other native species of the prairies. Prairie grasses are an important part of our heritage and underlie our very existence.

There are many grassy places in nature today. Some are fescue pastures, Kentucky bluegrass lawns, and hay meadows containing various grass mixtures of foreign introductions. Such places contain almost wholly non-native species, and this separates them from prairie which is made up entirely of native grasses and herbs. A well-developed prairie makes no accommodation to foreign introductions. Only when prairie has been weakened does it allow entry of outside or foreign elements. Woody species seldom are present in prairie in any significant number, except at margins of prairie where the prairie contacts the forest, or up the ravines where added protection is given to woody species.

The quality of a prairie is proportional to the protection and care it has received. Once a good prairie has been seen and its composition and structure understood, then judging the quality of another is made easier. Excessive or uncontrolled use degrades a prairie. Grazing, herbiciding, mowing, plowing, drainage, and lack of fire affect all prairie species. Each kind of disturbance affects the prairie species somewhat differently. Each species has its own limits of tolerance to various factors. Some species are deep rooted and have abundant food reserves; other species are unpalatable and escape grazing. Such species last longer in prairies than others. These remaining species are called relicts, and they give us clues as to what kind of vegetation once occupied the area.

The quality of a prairie is often judged by the native species which remain, although this is not always the case. One must get to know the native species. Look for a well developed structure such as layering, well marked communities, and well marked seasonal aspects. The dark soil of a former prairie or a relict prairie will reflect the occupation of the area by grasses. Conversely, a lack of any of these features, or the presence of bare soil, erosion, or the presence of annual or invading species among a few relict prairie species, often reflects a degenerated prairie.

In our rush to settle the land, only a few prairies and some remnants remain. Both the relict prairies, and the remnants which remain, are worthy of our best efforts to maintain, increase, study, and enjoy.

Collecting, Treating, and Using
Seeds of Prairie Plants

The past few years have seen a revival of interest in preserving prairies and in starting new prairies from the planting of seeds of indigenous prairie plants. These planted prairies have been started and cared for by workers within educational institutions, corporate bodies, departments of transportation, departments of conservation, and by individual citizens who desire them as a kind of "wild garden" of their own.

Only a few commercial sources of prairie seed exist, and the demand is often greater than the supply. A difficulty in the use of commercial seed is that it is often produced far from where it is to be used. This may cause some problems in the adaptability of the plants to conditions where they are planted, and in creating the authenticity of the prairie in that particular place.

Lighter weight of some prairie grass seed makes harvest by machine difficult. Handstripping is often more feasible if the project is not too large. The seeds of the major prairie grass dominants are usually easily available from nearby degraded prairie remnants such as those found along highways and railroad rights-of-way. The grass seed should be gathered and stored in cloth bags in the autumn. Good stands have been achieved by planting during either spring or fall season. Upon germination in the fall, if enough growth is made to carry the plant through the winter, then growth during the following spring will be good and a suitable showing will be made the first year. Spring planting on the other hand will produce a result which may cause one to wonder if a good start has been made. It may take a high mowing or two of the weeds which accompany the grasses to reduce competition, and the degree to which the grasses have become established will not really be evident until the second year.

If the grass seed is to be stored for outdoor use during a year following its collection, it should be stored in a cool dry place and fumigated with insect repellent crystals such as paradichlorobenzene. A moist-cold treatment is beneficial about three months before planting. This treatment may be made by placing the seeds in an equal volume of moist vermiculite at a temperature a few degrees above freezing and below a temperature where molds will grow. This is about 38 degrees and 34 degrees Fahrenheit. The seeds and vermiculite can be broadcast or sown together.

Forb seeds can be stratified in a similar way. Forbs are best planted in flats in a greenhouse or in 2″ x 2″ peat pots. At transplanting time, the forbs may be spaced as desired in the field. Late spring is a good time for forb transplanting. Forb seeds can be successfully gathered by hand, and good quality of that seed may be had by collecting it shortly after flowering when it is mature and before insects or disease have ravaged it. Seeds which are carefully gathered, cleaned, and sorted will give good performance.

Suitable germination may be achieved without special treatment for a number of prairie forbs, and relatively simple treatment will induce germination for several others. The seeds of the following prairie forbs have been found to germinate without special treatment:

Prairie Leadplant *(Amorpha canescens)*
Windflower *(Anemone cylindrica)*
Purple Coneflower *(Echinacea purpurea)*
Silky Aster *(Aster sericeus)*
Three-flowered Avens *(Geum triflorum)*
Red Prairie Lily *(Lilium philadelphicum)*
Bush Lespedeza *(Lespedeza capitata)*

Clustered Poppy Mallow *(Callirhoë triangulata)*
Tickseed *(Coreopsis palmata)*

The following species have been found to respond to a moist-cold treatment of three months: poison hemlock *(Cicuta maculata),* late blooming gentian *(Gentiana puberulenta),* and western ironweed *(Vernonia fasciculata).*

Species responding to a moist-cold treatment of two months include the following:

Compass-plant *(Silphium laciniatum)*
Flat-topped Spurge *(Euphorbia corollata)*
Green Milkweed *(Asclepias viridiflora)*
Rough-leaved Sunflower *(Helianthus mollis)*
Prairie Dock *(Silphium terebinthinaceum)*
Blazing-star *(Liatris squarrosa)*
Tall Blazing-star *(Liatris pycnostachya)*
Golden Alexander *(Zizia aurea)*
Virginia Lespedeza *(Lespedeza virginica)*
Pussy-toes *(Antennaria* spp.)
Prairie Cinquefoil *(Potentilla arguta)*

Scarification of the following seeds achieves good germination:

Lead Plant *(Amorpha canescens)*
Canada Milkvetch *(Astragalus canadensis)*
White Prairie Clover *(Petalostemum candidum)*
Purple Prairie Clover *(Petalostemum purpureum)*
Clustered Poppy Mallow *(Callirhoë triangulata)*
Rattlebox *(Crotalaria sagittalis)*
Rough-leaved Onosmodium *(Onosmodium hispidissimum)*
Tall Baptisia *(Baptisia leucantha)*

The following plants as shown by their availability from nursery produced potted stock would indicate that they can be produced by seed:

Butterfly-weed *(Asclepias tuberosa)*
Sky-blue Aster *(Aster azureus)*
Smooth Aster *(Aster laevis)*
New England Aster *(Aster novae-angliae)*
Shooting-star *(Dodecatheon meadia)*
Pale Coneflower *(Echinacea pallida)*
Rattlesnake Master *(Eryngium yuccifolium)*
Wild Strawberry *(Fragaria virginiana)*

Closed Gentian *(Gentiana andrewsii)*
Ox-eye Sunflower *(Heliopsis helianthoides)*
Culver's-root *(Veronicastrum virginicum)*
Alumroot *(Heuchera richardsonii)*
Bluet *(Houstonia caerulea)*
Blazing-star *(Liatris aspera)*
Turk's-cap Lily *(Lilum michiganense)*
Feverfew *(Parthenium integrifolium)*
Prairie Phlox *(Phlox pilosa)*
Drooping Coneflower *(Ratibida pinnata)*
Compass-plant *(Silphium laciniatum)*
Prairie Dock *(Silphium terebinthinaceum)*
Rigid Goldenrod *(Solidago rigida)*

The main reasons for failure of germination include: seed coat too hard which offers mechanical resistance to expansion and emergence of the embryo; a need for after-ripening, or a change in acidity which results in certain metabolic change; seed coat too impermeable due to coverage with waxy or corky substances which interfere with absorption of water or in the exchange of gases. Some seeds may have been gathered with immature embryos.

The families of forbs most prominent in the prairie are the legume, composite, mint, and rose. Legumes characteristically have hard and mechanically resistant seed coats, as do some of the borages, mints, and umbellifers. The composites often have waxy, corky, husk-like coverings, which need to be removed for effective germination. Roses frequently require after-ripening. Germination of prairie forb seed is high enough with the proper treatment, if indeed treatment is needed, that one may be generally successful in establishing many different prairie forb species.

References

Blake, A. K. 1935. Viability and germination of seeds and early life history of prairie plants. Ecological Monographs 5:405-460.

Christiansen, P. A. 1967. Establishment of prairie species in Iowa by seeding and transplanting. Ph.D. Dissertation, Iowa State University.

Mayer, A. M. and A. Poljakoff-Mayber. 1963. The Germination of Seeds. The Macmillan Co., New York, N.Y. p. 61-98.

Nicholas, G. E. 1934. The influence of exposure to winter temperature upon seed germination in various native North American Plants. Ecology 15:364-373.

Rock, H. W. 1974. Prairie propagation handbook. Boerner Botanical Gardens, Milwaukee, Wisconsin. 76 pp.

Schramm, Peter. 1968. (editor) Proceedings of a Symposium on Prairie and Prairie Restoration, Knox College, Galesburg, Illinois.

Schramm, Peter. 1976. The "Do's and Dont's" of Prairie Restoration. Proceedings of the Fifth Midwest Prairie Conference, Iowa State University, pp. 139-150.

Sorenson, J. T. and D. J. Holden. 1974. Germination of native prairie forb seeds. Journal of Range Management 27:123-126.

Voigt, John W. 1977. Seed germination of true prairie forbs. Journal of Range Management 30:439-441.

Illustrated Glossary

In order to distinguish one kind of prairie plant from another, it is necessary to learn the major characteristics which these prairie plants of Illinois may possess. Illustrated on the next few pages are several of the most commonly encountered characteristics of leaves, flowers, and their arrangement (characters 1-4). A thorough understanding of these structures will insure a quicker and more accurate identification.

On the pages following the illustrated glossary and glossary are keys to the prairie plants of Illinois. A key is a botanical device which enables the user, through proper selection of a series of choices, to identify a specimen at hand. Begin with the first pair of number 1's, choose the statement that best fits the unknown specimen, and then go to the next correct pair of statements. Continue this procedure until the name of the plant is reached.

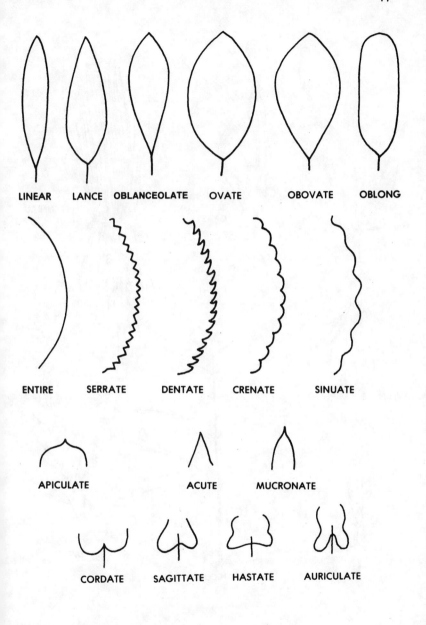

Character 1
LEAF CHARACTERISTICS

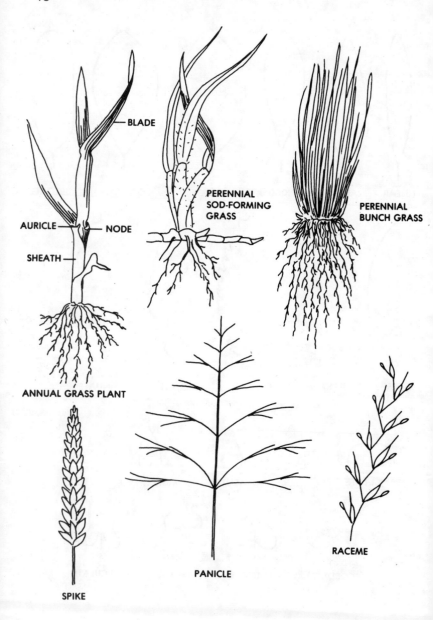

BLADE

AURICLE — NODE

SHEATH

PERENNIAL
SOD-FORMING
GRASS

PERENNIAL
BUNCH GRASS

ANNUAL GRASS PLANT

SPIKE

PANICLE

RACEME

Character 2
LEAF ARRANGEMENTS

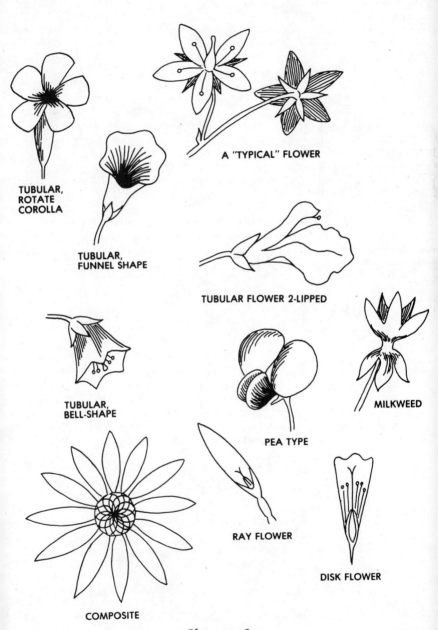

TUBULAR, ROTATE COROLLA

TUBULAR, FUNNEL SHAPE

A "TYPICAL" FLOWER

TUBULAR FLOWER 2-LIPPED

TUBULAR, BELL-SHAPE

PEA TYPE

MILKWEED

COMPOSITE

RAY FLOWER

DISK FLOWER

Character 3
FLOWER CHARACTERISTICS

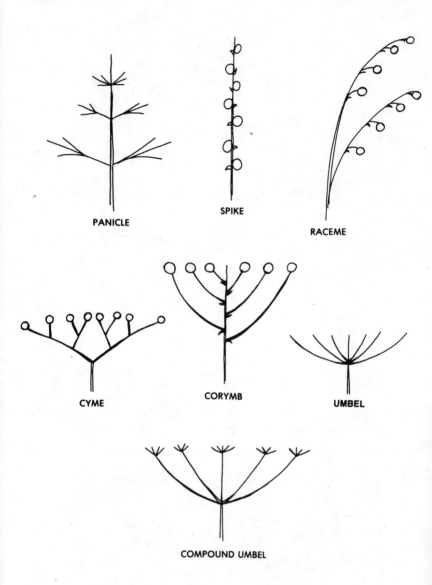

PANICLE

SPIKE

RACEME

CYME

CORYMB

UMBEL

COMPOUND UMBEL

Character 4
FLOWER ARRANGEMENTS

Glossary

achene. A one-seeded, dry fruit.

acuminate. Gradually tapering to a point.

acute. Sharply tapering to a point.

auricle. An ear-like lobe.

awn. A bristle usually terminating a structure.

bract. An accessory structure at the base of many flowers, usually appearing leaflike.

calyx. All the sepals of a flower.

catkin. A spike of unisexual flowers without petals.

ciliate. Bearing marginal hairs.

connate. Union of like parts.

cordate. Heart-shaped.

corolla. That part of the flower composed of the petals.

corona. A crown of petal-like structures.

corymb. A cluster of flowers where the stalked flowers are arranged along an elongated axis but with the flowers all attaining about the same height.

corymbose. Having a corymb.

culm. A stem which has one or more flowers at its end.

cyme. A type of broad and flat cluster of flowers in which the central flowers bloom first.

dentate. With sharp teeth which project outward.

discoid. Having only disk flowers.

entire. Said of a leaf edge which has no teeth.

floret. A small flower.

glomerule. A small compact cluster.

glume. A sterile scale subtending a spikelet.

hastate. Spear-shaped.

head. A congested cluster of sessile flowers.

inferior. Referring to the position of the ovary when it is embedded in the receptacle.

inflorescence. A cluster of flowers.

involute. Rolled inward.

lanceolate. Lance-shaped.

latex. Milky sap.

lemma. A scale subtending a grass flower.

ligule. A structure on the inner surface of the leaf of a grass at the junction of the blade and sheath.

linear. Narrowly elongated and uniform in width throughout.

neutral. Said of a flower which has neither stamens nor pistils.

oblanceolate. Reversely lance-shaped.

oblong. Broadest at the middle and tapering to both ends, but broader than elliptic.

obovate. Reversely egg-shaped.

obtuse. Rounded.

orbicular. Round.

oval. Broadly elliptic.

ovary. The lower swollen part of the pistil.

ovate. Egg-shaped.

ovoid. A solid object which is egg-shaped.

palmate. Divided radiately like the fingers of a hand.

panicle. A cluster of flowers arranged in a series of racemes.

pedicel. The stalk of a flower.

peduncle. The stalk of a cluster of flowers.

perfect. Said of a flower which has both stamens and pistils.

perfoliate. Referring to a leaf which appears to have the stem pass through it.

perianth. Those parts of a flower including the sepals and petals.

petiolate. Having a leaf-stalk.

petiole. The stalk of a leaf.

pinnate. Divided once into distinct stamens.

pinnatifid. Said of a simple leaf which is cleft or lobed only part way to its axis.

pistillate. Referring to the pistil parts of the plant.

plumose. Feathery.

pubescence. Hairiness.

pubescent. Hairy.

raceme. A cluster of flowers whose stalked flowers are arranged along an elongated axis.

racemose. Having a raceme.

rachis. The axis to which the flowers are attached.

receptacle. That part of the flower to which the perianth, stamens, and pistils are usually attached.

reniform. Kidney-shaped.

rhizome. A horizontal, underground stem.

rosette. A cluster of leaves in a circular arrangement at the base of a plant.

scabrous. Rough to the touch.

scape. A leafless stalk bearing a flower or inflorescence.

serrate. With teeth which project forward.

serrulate. With small teeth which project forward.

sessile. Without a stalk.

spatulate. Oblong, but with the basal end elongated.

spicate. Possessing a spike.

spike. A cluster of flowers where sessile flowers are arranged along an elongated axis.

spikelet. A small spike.

stamen. The pollen-producing organ of the flower.

staminate. Referring to the pollen-producing parts of the plant.

stipule. A leaf-like structure found at the point of attachment of a leaf to the stem.

style. The elongated part of the pistil between the pistil and the stigma.

terete. Round in cross-section.

ternately. Divided into three parts.

tomentum. Wool.

trifoliolate. With 3 leaflets.

umbel. A flower cluster where all the flower stalks arise from the same level.

umbellate. Possessing an umbel.

verticillate. Whorled.

viscid. Sticky.

whorl. An arrangement of three or more structures at a point on the stem.

Key to the Groups of Prairie Plants

1. Plants with leaves long and narrow, at least ten times longer than broad; leaves with parallel veins 2
1. Plants with leaves usually not ten times longer than broad, but if leaves are ten times longer than broad, then the leaves with net veins 3
   2. Plants with conspicuous flower parts, these either yellow, lavender, purple, white, or blue . . . . . . Group E
   2. Plants with inconspicuous green or straw-colored or brownish flowers having no petals . . . . Group F
3. All the leaves confined to the base of the plant . . . . Group A
3. Leaves borne along the stem, although basal leaves may also be present .4
   4. Leaves, or some of them, compound, that is, divided into 3 or more distinct segments, or leaf-lets . . . . Group B
   4. Leaves all simple, that is, not divided into distinct segments, or leaflets, although the leaves may be lobed 5
5. Leaves whorled or opposite on the stem . . . . Group C
5. Leaves alternate on the stem . . . . Group D

GROUP A

All the leaves confined to the base of the plant; leaves not long and narrow, never ten times longer than broad.

1. Some of all the leaves compound, that is, divided into distinct segments, or leaflets 2
1. Leaves all simple, although sometimes toothed or lobed . . .3
    2. Leaflets 3, 1 cm or more wide; flowers white . . . .
        . . . . *Fragaria americana*
    2. Leaflets several, very narrow, always less than 5 mm wide; flowers purple . . . . *Viola pedatifida*
3. Leaves deeply palmately divided into numerous narrow lobes
    . . . . *Viola pedatifida*
3. Leaves not deeply lobed, although sometimes with a large tooth on either side near the base .4
    4. Leaves large, 15 or more cm wide, rough to the touch; flowers borne in yellow heads . . *Silphium terebinthinaceum*
    4. Leaves less than 10 cm across, not rough to the touch, although sometimes hairy; flowers not borne in yellow heads 5
5. Leaves without any teeth, tapering gradually into broad petioles; petals pointing backward . . . . . . *Dodecatheon meadia*
5. Leaves with broad scallops around the margin, or with a large tooth on either side near the base 6
    6. Leaves with broad scallops around the margin; flowers very small, greenish . . . . *Heuchera richardsonii*
    6. Leaves with a large tooth on either side near the base; flowers up to 2 cm across, purple . . . . *Viola sagittata*

GROUP B

Leaves or some of them compound, that is, divided into 3 or more distinct segments, or leaflets.

1. Flowers white or cream-colored 2
1. Flowers yellow, blue, lavender, rose, purple, or pink 8
    2. Leaves divided into 3, 5, or 7 segments, or leaflets . . .3

2. Leaves divided into 9 or more segments, or leaflets . . . .
. . . . *Cicuta maculata*

3. Flowers shaped like little sweet peas, asymmetrical; leaflets without teeth along the edges 4

3. Flowers with 5-several petal-like sepals surrounding a central core of pistils, symmetrical; leaflets usually with some irregular teeth 7

    4. Leaflets 5-7; flowers small, in densely crowded spikes . .
    . . . .*Petalostemum candidum*

    4. Leaflets 3; flowers at least 7 mm long, less crowded in an elongated inflorescence 5

5. Flowers up to 1 cm long, with a purple dot . . . .
. . . . *Lespedeza capitata*

5. Flowers over 1 cm long, without a purple dot 6

    6. Plants smooth; pods smooth, up to 3 cm long . . . .
    . . . .*Baptisia leucantha*

    6. Plants usually hairy; pods hairy, usually at least 4 cm long
    . . . .*Baptisia leucophaea*

7. Plants arising from a tuber; petal-like sepals 10-20 . . . .
. . . .*Anemone caroliniana*

7. Plants arising from a rhizome; petal-like sepals 5 (-6) . . . . .
. . . .*Anemone canadensis*

    8. Flowers yellow 9

    8. Flowers blue, lavender, purple, rose, or pink 11

9. Flowers borne in heads, with several yellow rays surrounding an elongated central column . . . .*Ratibida pinnata*

9. Flowers borne in loose clusters, in umbels, or solitary . . .10

    10. Flowers borne in umbels; each flower less than 1 cm across; stamens 5 . . . .*Polytaenia nuttallii*

    10. Flowers solitary or in small clusters; each flower more than 1 cm across; stamens 10 . . . . . .*Cassia fasciculata*

11. Plants woody, with some prickles on the stem; flowers rose-colored . . . .*Rosa carolina*

11. Plants herbaceous, without prickles on the stem; flowers blue, lavender, purple, or pink and cream 12

    12. Leaflets 3 or 5 13

    12. Leaflets 7 to many .16

13. Leaflets with a few glandular dots (best seen by holding leaf to light) 14

13. Leaflets without glandular dots 15

    14. Leaflets always 3 . . . .*Psoralea psoralioides*

14. Leaflets sometimes 5 . . . . *Psoralea tenuiflora*
15. Flowers in an elongated, cylindrical head; leaflets sometimes 5 . . . . *Petalostemum purpureum*
15. Flowers loosely clustered; leaflets always 3 . . . .
. . . . *Lespedeza virginica*
  16. Flowers pea-shaped 17
  16. Flowers not pea-shaped, symmetrical 18
17. Flowers pink and cream; leaves with an uneven number of leaflets . . . . *Tephrosia virginiana*
17. Flowers bluish-purple; leaves with an even number of leaflets . . . . *Vicia americana*
  18. Leaves palmately divided . . . . *Anemone patens*
  18. Leaves pinnately divided, with small leaf segments between the regular leaflets . . . . *Geum triflorum*

GROUP C

Leaves opposite or whorled, simple.

1. Leaves whorled 2
1. Leaves opposite 4
  2. Leaves toothed; flowers in an elongated, candelabra-like inflorescence . . . . *Veronicastrum virginicum*
  2. Leaves entire; flowers in umbels or racemes 3
3. Flowers in umbels; latex present . . . . . *Asclepias verticillata*
3. Flowers in racemes; latex absent . . . . . . *Galium tinctorium*
  4. Flowers with an hour-glass shape; latex present 5
  4. Flowers not with an hour-glass shape; latex absent 7
5. Flowers purple; leaves broadly rounded or subcordate at the base . . . . *Asclepias sullivantii*
5. Flowers greenish; leaves tapering to the base 6
  6. Each umbel of flowers borne on an elongated stalk . . . .
. . . . *Asclepias hirtella*
  6. Each umbel of flowers sessile or nearly so . . . .
. . . . *Asclepias viridiflora*
7. Flowers yellow 8
7. Flowers deep blue, pink, purple, or white with purple dots
. 16
  8. Flowers borne single, with distinct yellow petals . . . . . .
. . . . *Lysimachia ciliata*
  8. Flowers borne several in a head, the head usually com-

posed of several tubular flowers in a central disk, surrounded by several ray flowers 9
9. Leaves deeply 3-lobed . . . . *Coreopsis palmata*
9. Leaves without lobes 10
  10. Each flower head with several rows of green leaf-like
      bracts on the outside 11
  10. Each flower head with 1 or 2 rows of green leaf-like bracts
      on the outside 12
11. Leaves completely clasping the stem so as to form cup-shaped
    cavities . . . . *Silphium perfoliatum*
11. Leaves sessile or short petiolate, but never clasping the stem
    . . . . *Silphium integrifolium*
  12. Leaf-like bracts on the outside of each flower head obtuse;
      ray flowers fertile, long persistent *Heliopsis helianthoides*
  12. Leaf-like bracts on the outside of each flower head acute;
      ray flowers sterile, not long persistent 13
13. Central disk of each flower head red or purple . . . .
    . . . . *Helianthus rigidus*
13. Central disk of each flower head yellow 14
  14. Stems smooth or nearly so below the flower heads . . . .
      . . . . *Helianthus grosseserratus*
  14. Stems hairy 15
15. Leaves densely gray-hairy on both surfaces *Helianthus mollis*
15. Leaves not densely gray-hairy, although they may have some
    hairs . . . . *Helianthus tuberosus*
  16. Flowers white, with purple dots 17
  16. Flowers pink, blue, or purple 18
17. Stems smooth; leaves up to 5 mm broad . . . .
    . . . . *Pycnanthemum tenuifolium*
17. Stems hairy; leaves (or most of them) over 5 mm broad . . . .
    . . . . *Pycnanthemum virginianum*
  18. Flowers 2-lipped, distinctly asymmetrical 19
  18. Flowers not 2-lipped, mostly symmetrical 20
19. Flowers crowded in dense globular heads nearly as wide as
    high, or wider . . . . *Monarda fistulosa*
19. Flowers clustered in an elongated spike considerably longer
    than broad . . . . *Teucrium canadense*
  20. Leaves toothed; flowers slightly asymmetrical . . . .
      . . . . *Buchnera americana*
  20. Leaves entire; flowers perfectly symmetrical 21

21. Stamens 4 . . . . *Ruellia humilis*
21. Stamens 5 22
  22. Corolla abruptly narrowed below the lobes into a very slender tube . . . . *Phlox pilosa*
  22. Corolla scarcely tapering below the lobes 23
23. Stems hairy; corolla open at the top . . *Gentiana puberulenta*
23. Stems smooth; corolla nearly closed at the top . . . .
  . . . .*Gentiana andrewsii*

GROUP D

Leaves alternate, simple.

1. Flowers crowded together in a head, each flower sharing a common receptacle 2
1. Flowers borne individually, each with its own receptacle .24
  2. Flowers white, whitish-green, or cream 3
  2. Flowers blue, purple, violet, or yellow 8
3. Heads composed of both ray flowers and disk flowers 4
3. Heads composed only of disk flowers 5
  4. Rays 15-25, usually at least 1 cm long; leaves linear to linear-lanceolate . . . .*Aster ericoides*
  4. Rays 5, less than 1 cm long; leaves ovate to ovate-oblong . . . .*Parthenium intergrifolium*
5. Leaves (at least the lower surface) and stems covered with dense white wool 6
5. Leaves and stems not white-woolly 7
  6. Most of the leaves clustered in a basal rosette; leaves on the stem linear; heads 4-6 mm across . . .*Antennaria neglecta*
  6. Leaves not clustered in a basal rosette; leaves on the stem lanceolate to oblong; heads 2-3 mm across . . . .*Artemisia ludoviciana* var. *gnaphalodes*
7. Plants smooth; lower leaves oval to ovate, long petiolate; upper leaves ovate to oblong, sessile . . . .*Cacalia tuberosa*
7. Plants hairy; all leaves similar, lanceolate to linear-lanceolate . . . .*Brickellia eupatorioides*
  8. Flowers purple or pink 9
  8. Flowers yellow 17
9. Heads with both ray and disk flowers 10
9. Heads with only disk flowers 15

10. Rays pink, turned downward; disk conical, brownish-black ....*Echinacea pallida*

10. Rays purple, spreading; disk flat, yellow 11

11. Basal or lowest leaves heart-shaped ....*Aster azureus*

11. Basal or lowest leaves not heart-shaped 12

   12. Stem-leaves clasping at the base 13

   12. Stem-leaves not clasping at the base ....*Aster sericeus*

13. Stems smooth ....*Aster laevis*

13. Stems hairy, at least in the upper part 14

   14. Leaves strongly clasping; rays 40 or more ....
..................*Aster novae-angliae*

   14. Leaves barely clasping; rays usually 20-30 ....
.................*Aster oblongifolius*

15. Heads in a dense spike 15 cm or more long ....
.....................*Liatris pycnostachya*

15. Heads usually solitary in the axils of the leaves, 1-3 cm long
..................................16

   16. Bracts on outside of flower heads rounded at the tip, appressed ....*Liatris aspera*

   16. Bracts on outside of flower heads pointed at the tip, projecting outward ....*Liatris squarrosa*

17. All leaves deeply pinnately lobed, the leaves usually 15 cm or more broad ....*Silphium laciniatum*

17. Leaves unlobed or only shallowly lobed, never 15 cm broad
..................................18

   18. Basal leaves unlobed, stem-leaves shallowly lobed ....
.....................*Senecio pauperculus*

   18. All leaves unlobed 19

19. Heads with yellow rays 1 cm or more long 20

19. Heads with yellow rays rarely longer than 5 mm 22

   20. Heads with a brown-black, low-conical center ....
.....................*Rudbeckia hirta*

   20. Heads with a yellow, flattened center 21

21. Stems smooth or nearly so .....*Helianthus grosseserratus*

21. Stems hairy ....*Helianthus tuberosus*

   22. Leaves linear to linear-lanceolate, up to 6 mm wide ...
.....................*Solidago graminifolia*

   22. Leaves ovate, elliptic, lanceolate, or oblanceolate ...23

23. Leaves lanceolate or oblanceolate, strongly 3-nerved from the base ....*Solidago canadensis*

23. Leaves ovate to elliptic, not conspicuously 3-nerved from the base . . . . *Solidago rigida*
   24. Plants with latex 25
   24. Plants without latex 27
25. Flowers white, not hour-glass shaped . . *Euphorbia corollata*
25. Flowers green, hour-glass shaped 26
   26. Each umbel of flowers borne on an elongated stalk . . . .
   . . . . *Asclepias hirtella*
   26. Each umbel of flowers sessile or nearly so . . . .
   . . . . *Asclepias viridiflora*
27. Plants small shrubs 28
27. Plants herbaceous; flowers with petals or petal-like structures
  29
   28. Leaves with one main vein . . . . *Salix humilis*
   28. Leaves with three veins from the base, all about the same size . . . . *Ceanothus americana*
29. Flowers orange or yellow 30
29. Flowers purple, pale blue, or cream 32
   30. Flowers hour-glass shaped, orange . . *Asclepias tuberosa*
   30. Flowers not hour-glass shaped, yellow to yellow-orange
  31
31. Petals 4, free from each other, yellow; flowers 2 cm or more across . . . . *Oenothera pilosella*
31. Petals 5, attached to each other, yellow-orange; flowers less than 2 cm across . . . . *Lithospermum canescens*
   32. Flowers purple; leaves triangular, large . . . .
   . . . . *Callirhoe triangulata*
   32. Flowers cream-colored or light blue; leaves not triangular, small 33
33. Flowers cream-colored, borne in umbel-like inflorescences .
   . . . . *Comandra richardsiana*
33. Flowers pale blue, borne in a spike . . . . *Lobelia spicata*

GROUP E

Plants with leaves long and narrow, at least ten times longer than broad; leaves with parallel veins; flowers conspicuous, yellow, lavender, purple, blue, orange, or white.

1. Leaves with spine-like teeth; flowers white, borne in spherical heads ....*Eryngium yuccifolium*
1. Leaves without teeth; flowers variously colored but not white, not borne in spherical heads 2
    2. Flowers yellow or orange 3
    2. Flowers blue, purple, or lavender 5
3. Flowers yellow, up to 2 cm across; leaves all basal, hairy ...
    ....*Hypoxis hirsuta*
3. Flowers orange, more than 4 cm across; leaves borne on the stem 4
    4. Flowers erect; only the uppermost group of leaves in a whorl; plants less than 1 meter tall ....
        ....*Lilium philadelphicum* var. *andinum*
    4. Flowers nodding; several whorls of leaves borne on the stem; plants generally over 1 meter tall ....
        ....*Lilium michiganense*
5. Flowers large, 5 cm or more across, with petal-like styles ..6
5. Flowers small, up to 2.5 cm across, with the styles not petal-like 7
    6. Flowers borne on erect stems; ovary and fruit 3-angled ..
        ....*Iris shrevei*
    6. Flowers borne near the ground; ovary and fruit 6-angled .
        ....*Iris brevicaulis*
7. Stems winged; stamens 3; ovary inferior *Sisyrinchium albidum*
7. Stems unwinged; stamens 6; ovary superior 8
    8. Sepals and petals the same color; stalks bearing the anthers smooth ....*Camassia scilloides*
    8. Sepals green, petals blue or lavender; stalks bearing the anthers with long hairs 9
9. Stems generally 40-100 cm tall; leaves and stems glabrous and glaucous; sepals glabrous or with a tuft of eglandular hairs at the tip ....*Tradescantia ohiensis*
9. Stems generally 5-40 cm tall; leaves and stems glabrous or pubescent, but not glaucous; sepals pubescent throughout with glandular or eglandular hairs 10

10. Hairs of the sepals eglandular . . *Tradescantia virginiana*
10. Hairs of the sepals glandular . . . *Tradescantia bracteata*

GROUP F

Plants with leaves long and narrow, at least ten times longer than broad; leaves with parallel veins; flowers inconspicuous, green or brown or straw-colored, without petals.

1. Leaves borne in 3 ranks; staminate flowers borne separately from pistillate flowers 2
1. Leaves borne in 2 ranks; staminate flowers and pistillate flowers borne together (except in *Tripsacum dactyloides*) 4
    2. All heads similar in size and shape . . . . . *Carex bicknellii*
    2. Some heads elongated, bearing staminate flowers, other heads more spherical, bearing pistillate flowers 3
3. Fruiting structures hairy . . . . *Carex pensylvanica*
3. Fruiting structures smooth . . . . *Carex meadii*
    4. Spikelets bearing six perianth parts 5
    4. Spikelets without perianth parts, the flowers, instead, subtended by scales 6
5. Flowers borne in spherical heads; plants over 50 cm tall . . .
    . . . . *Juncus torreyi*
5. Flowers borne along an elongated axis; plants usually less than 30 cm tall . . . . *Juncus tenuis*
    6. Staminate and pistillate flowers borne separately; leaves 15-30 mm broad . . . . *Tripsacum dactyloides*
    6. Staminate and pistillate flowers borne together; leaves rarely over 15 mm broad .7
7. Spikelets bearing one or more awns (bristle- or thread-like extensions from the apex) at least 3 mm long 8
7. Spikelets without awns 15
    8. Spikelets arranged in unbranched, dense spikes 9
    8. Spikelets arranged in racemes or panicles (these sometimes condensed) 10
9. Spikes 10-25 cm long; awns usually more than 15 mm long; plants perennial, to 2 meters tall . . . . . . *Elymus canadensis*
9. Spikes 2-7 cm long; awns less than 15 mm long; plants annual, to 35 cm tall . . . . *Hordeum pusillum*

34

21. Spikelets pointed at the tip, smooth 22
    22. Leaves 2-6 mm wide; all scales of the spikelets similar in shape and texture . . . .*Sporobolus cryptandrus*
    22. Leaves usually 8-15 mm wide; one of the scales of the spikelet much smaller than the others 23
23. Spikelets 2.0-2.5 mm long; plants mostly 1-2 meters tall . . .
. . . .*Panicum virgatum*
23. Spikelets 3.5-6.0 mm long; plants up to 75 cm tall . . . .
. . . .*Panicum capillare*

LEADPLANT
(*Amorpha canescens* Pursh)

Season and Stature: Leadplant is also known as Prairie Shoestring because of its deep roots which often penetrate to depths of fifteen feet or more. The name Leadplant is given because of the plant's lead-gray foliage. It is a warm-season or Summer perennial, somewhat shrubby, belonging to the Leguminosae, or legume family. Leadplant reaches a height of some 80 to 100 cm.

Flowers: The flowers of Leadplant are small, medium to dark purple, and densely aggregated in the racemose inflorescence.

Leaves: The lead-gray leaves are pinnately compound with some 21 to 51 leaflets which are covered with fine, gray hairs. Each leaflet is sessile and up to 1 cm broad.

Use or Importance: Leadplant is one of the most abundant upland herbs of prairie and closely associated throughout the prairies with the bluestem grasses. The plant is highly nutritious and palatable, and therefore decreases under heavy grazing. Hand-collected seeds can be germinated by weakening the seed coat. In restoration of prairie, the presence of this species is one of importance.

Habitat: Leadplant grows in sand prairies, hill prairies, and gravel-hill prairies.

Range: This species ranges from Michigan and Saskatchewan south to Arkansas, Texas, and New Mexico.

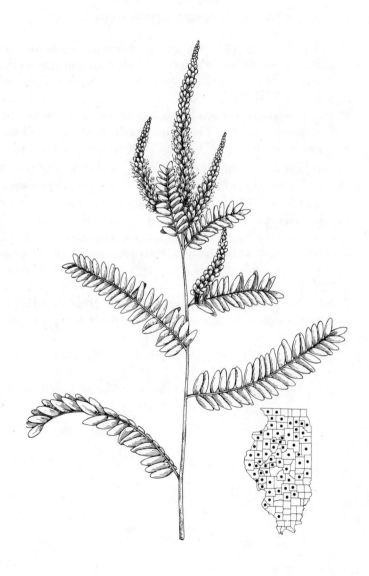

BIG BLUESTEM
(Andropogon gerardii Vitman)

Season and Stature: Big Bluestem is a native, warm-season perennial tall grass. It begins growth in late April and flowers in late summer, attaining heights up to 8 feet or sometimes more, including flower stalks.

Flowers: Spikelets are borne in pairs, one sessile, one pedicelled. The inflorescence is 3-branched, each of which is a raceme. Because of this, it has been called "turkey foot" bluestem.

Leaves: The lower leaf sheath of young growth has long hairs. The young shoots are somewhat flattened and the young culms are oval in cross-section.

Use or Importance: This was a chief component of the original prairie and was used for grazing or as a hay meadow. It decreases under heavy grazing. Prairies heavily grazed usually degenerate to lower condition because of competitive benefit to less palatable species.

Habitat: Big Bluestem is a lowland dominant. It grows in moist soil, sometimes on the lower slopes and sparingly on uplands.

Range: This species caused the eastern, humid prairies to be called "bluestem prairie," or "tall grass prairie." It is a major dominant in the True Prairie. It is found in Mixed Prairie in ravines and valley bottoms. It is also found southward into the Texas Prairie.

CANADIAN ANEMONE
(*Anemone canadensis* L.)

Season and Stature: The Canadian Anemone, a member of the Ranunculaceae, or crowfoot family, is a native, cool-season perennial which attains a height up to 60 cm. It flowers during May and into the summer.

Flowers: The flower is 2.5 to 3.5 cm broad. There are 5 white perianth parts and numerous stamens and pistils. The flowers are generally not long lasting.

Leaves: The basal leaves are long-petioled, broader than long, 3- to 5-parted, and coarsely toothed. The veins are prominently netted. The upper leaves are sessile.

Use or Importance: The symmetrical beauty of the anemones is their greatest importance.

Habitat: Canadian Anemone occurs in moist soils of woods and prairies.

Range: This species ranges throughout most of North America north of Mexico.

CAROLINA ANEMONE
(*Anemone caroliniana* Walt.)

Season and Stature: Carolina Anemone is a native, cool-season perennial belonging to Ranunculaceae, or buttercup family. It grows to a height of 25 cm. Flowering is during the Spring aspect.

Flowers: The flowers, which are up to 2 cm across, are white to purplish. The perianth parts vary from 6 to 20.

Leaves: The basal leaves are slender, petioled, and divided into three divisions which are toothed or lobed. The leaves which subtend the flower are sessile and 3-cleft.

Use or Importance: All members of the genus *Anemone* have beauty and are a delight to the eye.

Habitat: Carolina Anemone is found in dry, open places, including prairies. In Illinois, it occurs in gravel prairies, loess hill prairies, roadsides, and other dry places.

Range: This species grows from North Carolina across the Midwest to South Dakota, south to Texas and Florida.

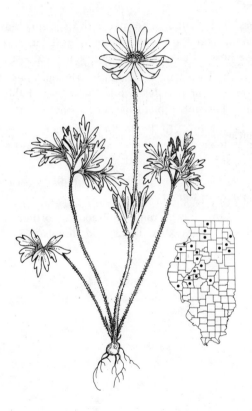

PASQUE-FLOWER
(*Anemone patens* L.)

Season and Stature: The Pasque-flower, a member of Ranuncula-ceae, or buttercup family, is a native, cool-season perennial herb which attains a height up to 20 cm. It flowers during the Spring aspect.

Flowers and Fruits: The perianth is light bluish-purple. The perianth segments are ovate-oblong. Fruits are clustered in a dense head of silky achenes with long plumose styles.

Leaves: The leaves are dissected into linear lobes. The basal leaves are on slender petioles, while the leaves of the upper stem are sessile. The entire plant has a covering of soft hairs.

Use or Importance: In the northern prairies, the Pasque-flower was eagerly looked for in flower and was regarded as a sign that the Spring season was at hand.

Habitat: In Illinois, this plant occurs in the gravel and hill prairies in the northern tier of counties.

Range: Pasque-flower ranges all across northern North America, south to New Mexico, Texas, and Illinois.

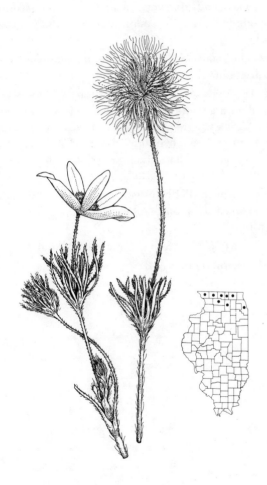

PRAIRIE SAGE

(*Artemisia ludoviciana* Nutt. var. *gnaphalodes* (Nutt.) T. & G.)

Season and Stature: The Prairie Sage, also called Western Sage, White Sage, and Mugwort, is a native, warm-season perennial, belonging to the family Compositae. It grows to a height of 30 to 100 cm.

Flowers: The small flowers are borne in spike-like panicles and are whitish-green.

Leaves: The leaves are the striking part of the plant. They are covered with a white tomentum on both sides, giving the whole plant a light gray-green color. The leaves are lanceolate, oblong, 2.5 to 8 cm long, and over 0.5 cm wide. The leaves may be entire, or the lower ones may be toothed or lobed. The leaves are narrowed into short petioles.

Use or Importance: Prairie Sage is frequent in garden plantings. It is often used as a border because of its silvery-white foliage contrast.

Habitat: Prairie Sage is found along highways and railroads.

Range: The natural range of this plant is across Canada from Quebec to British Columbia, south to Arkansas and Texas.

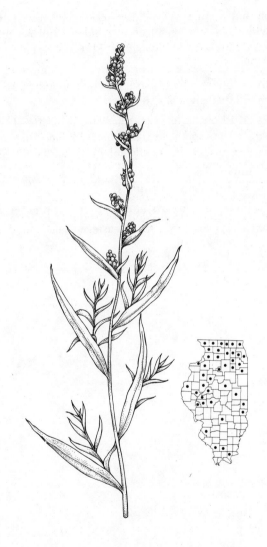

PUSSY-TOES
(Antennaria neglecta Greene)

Season and Stature: This Pussy-toes is a native perennial which reaches a height of 40 cm. It blooms during the Spring and Summer aspects. It belongs to the Compositae, or aster family.

Flowers: Each white flowering head is composed only of disk flowers. Several heads are grouped together at the top of a slender, sparsely leafy stem.

Leaves: Most of the leaves are in a basal rosette. These leaves are broader than the leaves found on the stem. They are covered on the lower surface by a cobwebby mass of white hairs.

Use or Importance: The flowers, which are long-persistent, have been used in winter bouquets.

Habitat: Pussy-toes occurs in dry ground of prairies and woods.

Range: This species ranges from eastern Canada to Alberta, south to Arizona and Virginia.

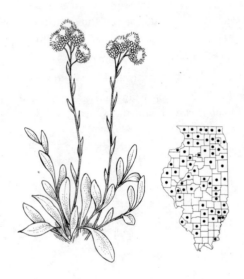

HAIRY GREEN MILKWEED
(*Asclepias hirtella* (Pennell) Woodson)

Season and Stature: The Hairy Green Milkweed is a native, warm-season perennial which may grow to a height of one meter. It flowers during the Summer aspect. It belongs to the Asclepiadaceae, or milkweed family.

Flowers: Hairy Green Milkweed has the typical hour-glass shaped flowers of milkweeds. Several greenish flowers are borne in groups from the axils of the leaves.

Leaves: The alternate or opposite leaves are linear to linear-lanceolate and rough to the touch. There is latex present.

Use or Importance: This species has little known economic importance.

Habitat: The Hairy Green Milkweed is an inhabitant of dry prairies.

Range: This species ranges from Michigan to Minnesota, south to Oklahoma and Louisiana.

SULLIVANT'S MILKWEED
(*Asclepias sullivantii* Engelm.)

Season and Stature: Sullivant's Milkweed is a native, warm-season perennial. It belongs to the Asclepiadaceae, or milkweed family. It may attain a height slightly over 1 meter. It flowers from July to September.

Flowers: The umbels are wide-spreading, mostly terminal, or sometimes in the upper axils. The purplish flowers are about 1 cm long.

Leaves: The thick leaves are sessile or on short petioles. They are oblong or ovate-oblong, with a mucronate tip. The veins are conspicuous and pinnate.

Use or Importance: Many species of milkweed offer possibilities for rubber production. Sullivant's Milkweed has such lactiferous potential.

Habitat: Sullivant's Milkweed occurs in moist prairies.

Range: This species ranges from Ontario to Minnesota, south to Ohio and Kansas. It is a member of the True Prairie.

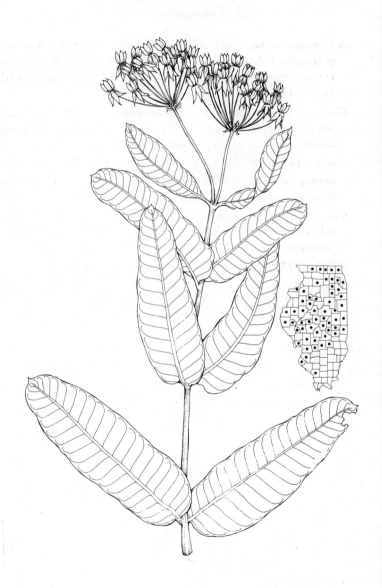

BUTTERFLY WEED
(*Asclepias tuberosa* L.)

Season and Stature: Butterfly Weed is a native, warm-season perennial which grows to a height up to 70 cm. It flowers in the Summer aspect and into the Fall. It belongs to the Asclepiadaceae, or milkweed family.

Flowers: The orange-colored flowers are borne in a broad umbel and, like all milkweed flowers, are pinched at the middle with 5 downward flexed petals and a corona at the top to give the flowers somewhat of an hour-glass shape.

Leaves: Unlike most milkweeds, this one has alternate leaves and, when plucked, the leaves do not exude a white latex as other milkweeds do. The sap of this milkweed is cream-colored and thin-looking in contrast to the sap of most other milkweeds. The leaves are tapered at each end and are without distinct petioles.

Use or Importance: This species can be propagated readily from seed, and has been used as a garden plant. It is reported that in its young stages it can be boiled as greens and that Indians used its roots as medicine. Livestock will not eat it by choice. It behaves as an increaser or invader on range land.

Habitat: Butterfly Weed grows in dry, open soil. It is abundant in prairies.

Range: This species ranges from New England to Minnesota, south to Arizona, Texas, and Florida.

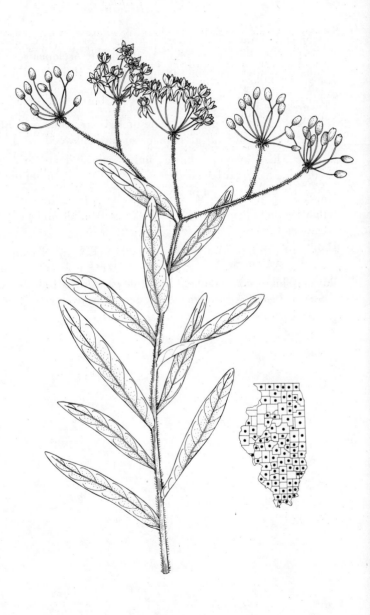

WHORLED MILKWEED
(*Asclepias verticillata* L.)

Season and Stature: The Whorled Milkweed is a native, warm-season perennial plant belonging to the family Asclepiadaceae. This milkweed attains a height of up to 60 cm. It flowers during the late Summer and Fall aspect.

Flowers: The flowers are greenish-white, borne on many-flowered umbels on slender pedicels. The umbels are numerous. Flowers have the typical hour-glass shape of the milkweed family.

Leaves: The leaves are linear and sessile and are arranged in verticillate or whorled clusters of 3 to 7. The margins of the leaves may be slightly rolled or involute.

Use or Importance: There is little known importance for this narrow-leaved member of the milkweed family.

Habitat: Whorled Milkweed is found in dry prairies, on hills, and in fields. In Illinois, it occurs in all dry types of prairie.

Range: This species ranges over the eastern half of the United States. It occurs throughout the True Prairie area.

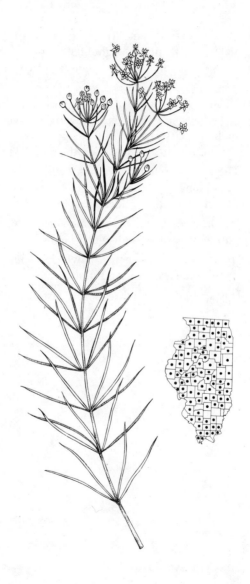

GREEN MILKWEED
(*Asclepias viridiflora* Raf.)

Season and Stature: Green Milkweed is a native, warm-season, perennial herb attaining a height of 30 to 90 cm. It flowers during June to September. Some botanists place it in the genus *Acerates.*

Flowers: The flowers are borne in dense terminal and axillary umbels. Pedicels are 4 to 8 mm long. The flowers are green and have an hour-glass shape. This shape is typical for milkweed flowers and is due to a structure on the flower known as a corona.

Leaves: The leaves are slightly rough to touch, alternate or opposite, oval, oblong, or ovate to lanceolate. The leaves are 2.5 to 12 cm long and up to 4 cm wide. They have short petioles.

Use or Importance: Little use is known for this striking green-flowered member of the milkweed family.

Habitat: In Illinois, the Green Milkweed is found in dry upland prairies, hill prairies, and sand prairies.

Range: This species is found over the eastern half of the United States.

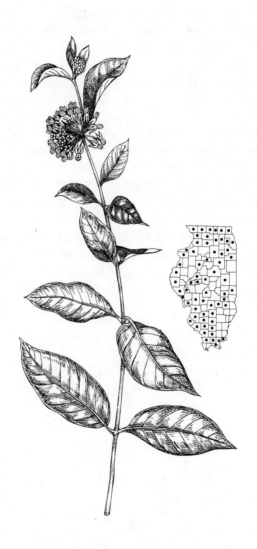

SKY-BLUE ASTER
(*Aster azureus* Lindl.)

Season and Stature: The Sky-blue Aster is a native, warm-season perennial species attaining a height of 30 to 100 cm. It blooms during the Fall aspect, from August to October.

Flowers: The heads are numerous and about 5 mm high. The rays, which are about 5 mm long, are bright blue and number from 10 to 20.

Leaves: The leaves are thick, entire, and rough on both sides. The basal and lower stem leaves are cordate and ovate, and measure from 5 to 15 cm long. They have slender petioles. The upper leaves have much shorter petioles.

Use or Importance: This blue-flowered aster is attractive and can be brought into wild home gardens. Sky-blue Aster decreases under grazing.

Habitat: The Sky-blue Aster occurs in both dry and moist prairies. It often is found where prairies border the woods.

Range: This species is found throughout the True Prairie and eastward to New York and Georgia.

HEATH ASTER
(*Aster ericoides* L.)

Season and Stature: The Heath, or Frost, Aster is a native, warm-season, late Summer and Fall blooming species. It attains a height up to 90 cm. It belongs to the Compositae, or aster family.

Flowers: The many white heads are somewhat less than one cm across. The heads are composed of white rays surrounding yellow disk flowers. Small green leaves are borne on the stalks bearing the heads.

Leaves: The leaves are small and linear to lanceolate. They are densely covered with short hairs.

Use or Importance: This plant has some importance because of its soil binding quality. It is not an important forage plant except when it is very young.

Habitat: Heath Aster grows in most dry, open areas, from woods to prairies to fields.

Range: This species ranges throughout the entire United States.

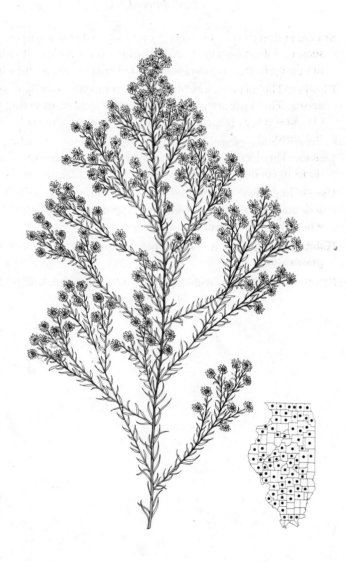

SMOOTH ASTER
(*Aster laevis* L.)

Season and Stature: The Smooth Aster is a warm-season perennial attaining a height up to one meter or more. It is a member of the Compositae, or aster family. It blooms during the Fall aspect.

Flowers: The heads are numerous, with 15 to 30 blue or violet rays. The heads are up to 2.5 cm broad.

Leaves: The leaves are smooth, with the upper ones sessile, usually cordate-clasping, lanceolate, oblong-lanceolate, acute or obtuse, up to 10 cm long, up to 2 cm wide. The basal leaves are gradually narrowed into winged petioles.

Use or Importance: The Smooth Aster takes easily to cultivation. It is a showy member of a wild garden.

Habitat: The Smooth Aster is found in moist or dry prairies, and in woods.

Range: Smooth Aster is distributed from Maine to Saskatchewan, south to Kansas, Louisiana, and Georgia.

AROMATIC ASTER
(*Aster oblongifolius* Nutt.)

Season and Stature: This late blooming aster is a native, warm-season perennial which attains a height up to 70 cm. It flowers from August to October.

Flowers: The several heads are about 2.5 cm broad, subtended by bracts which are linear-oblong, glandular, and aromatic. The rays are rose-purple, and number between 20 and 30.

Leaves: The leaves are oblong-lanceolate, sessile to partly clasping, and rough on both sides. They are 3 to 6 cm long.

Use or Importance: Aromatic Aster is palatable in its young growth and behaves as a decreaser when the prairie is grazed. The plant has been used for transplanting into gardens because of its beauty.

Habitat: This species occurs in upland prairies.

Range: Aromatic Aster grows from Pennsylvania to North Dakota, south to Texas, Alabama, and North Carolina.

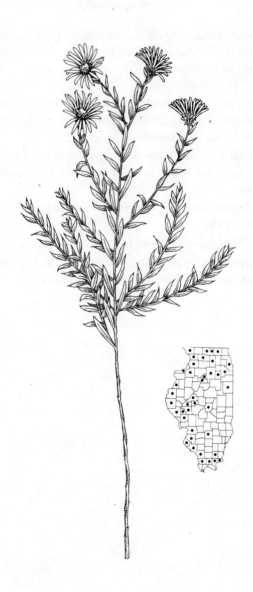

NEW ENGLAND ASTER
(*Aster novae-angliae* L.)

Season and Stature: New England Aster is a handsome warm-season perennial which attains a height of one meter or more. It blooms during the Summer and Fall aspects. It belongs to the Compositae, or aster family.

Flowers: Each head, which is up to 2.5 cm across, has a yellow disk surrounded by up to 100 narrow, bright purple rays. There are several heads in a terminal cluster.

Leaves: All the leaves are heart-shaped at the base and clasp the stem. They are rough to the touch and have no teeth along the margins.

Use or Importance: The colorful flowers of this species add beauty to the prairie.

Habitat: This species occurs in woods and prairies.

Range: New England Aster ranges from New England to North Dakota, south to New Mexico and Alabama.

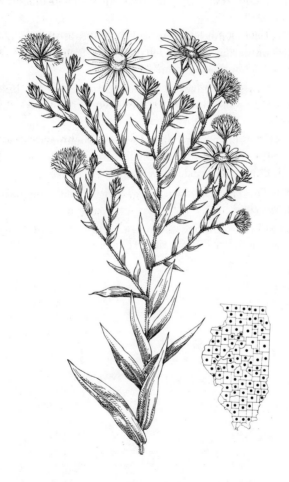

SILKY ASTER
(*Aster sericeus* Vent.)

Season and Stature: The Silky Aster, also called Silvery Aster, is a native, warm-season perennial belonging to the Compositae, or aster family. It attains a height up to 60 cm. It blooms during the Fall aspect.

Flowers: Silky Aster has beautiful lavender-purple or violet flowers. It has numerous heads, each one about 3 cm broad, with the rays per head numbering from 15 to 25.

Leaves: The stem leaves are sessile, broadest at the base, oblong, and entire. The surfaces of the leaves are covered with a dense silvery and silky pubescence.

Use or Importance: The plant decreases under grazing, hence its presence or absence indicates the condition of the prairie under the influence of grazing use.

Habitat: This species occurs in most dry habitats, including prairies and woods.

Range: Silky Aster ranges from Michigan to North Dakota, south to Texas, southern Illinois, and Tennessee.

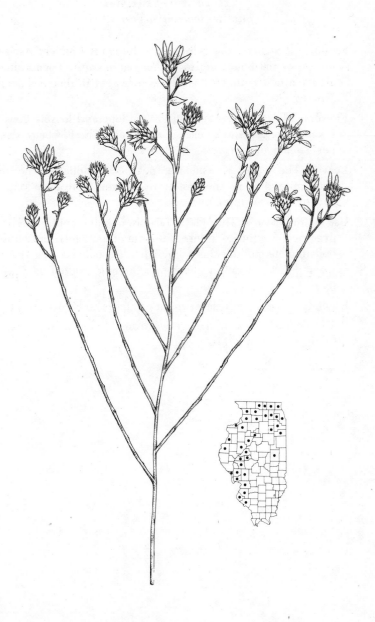

WHITE FALSE INDIGO
(*Baptisia leucantha* Torr. & Gray)

Season and Stature: The White False Indigo is a native, warm-season perennial belonging to the Leguminosae, or pea family. It attains a height up to 1 meter and flowers during the Summer aspect.

Flowers: The racemes are about 30 cm long and loosely flowered. Each flower is about 1 cm long and white. The flower is typically pea-shaped.

Leaves: The leaves are smooth, petioled, trifoliolate, becoming black upon drying. The leaflets are obovate, 1 to 2 cm long, and about half as wide as long.

Use or Importance: The White False Indigo apparently produces a dye used for indigo color. Both the leaves and the fruits are boiled or steeped for this color. The plant behaves as a decreaser when prairie is grazed, but the plant would seldom be grazed in its mature state.

Habitat: This species occurs in both prairies and woods.

Range: White False Indigo grows from Michigan to Minnesota, south to Texas and Mississippi.

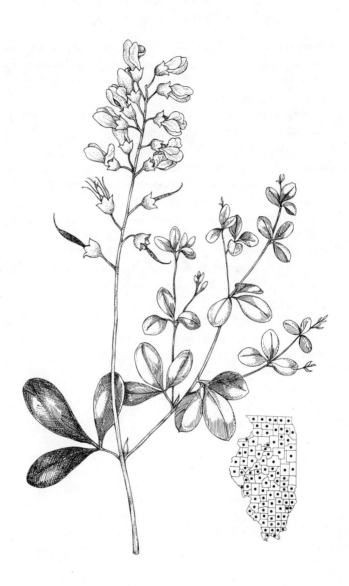

WILD FALSE INDIGO
(*Baptisia leucophaea* Nutt.)

Season and Stature: This robust herb, a member of the Leguminosae, or legume family, flowers during the Spring aspect. It achieves a height of 40 to 50 cm.

Flowers: The cream-colored, pea-shaped flowers are numerous along mostly horizontally extended racemes at the top of the plant. Each flower may be up to 3.0 cm long.

Leaves: Wild False Indigo leaflets are three in number and turn a blue-black color with the first frost. At season's end the plant detaches from the ground, but the leaves remain on the stem.

Use or Importance: A dye material of dark blue color has been extracted from the leaves and the fruits. This dye, however, is inferior to the real indigo dye. The plant is not important in providing forage. It is seldom selected for grazing, but it does decrease under long grazing use of prairie. Wild False Indigo is apparently slightly toxic, but affects the grazing animal only if eaten in quantity.

Habitat: This species occurs in prairies and in open woodlands.

Range: Wild False Indigo grows from Michigan south to Illinois and west to Minnesota, Nebraska, and Texas.

SIDE-OATS GRAMA
(*Bouteloua curtipendula* (Michx.) Torr.)

Season and Stature: When in flower during summer, the slender
flower stalks, from 30 to 90 cm tall, give the plant an overall
height which classes the plant as a mid-grass. Side-oats Grama is a
warm-season, tufted perennial whose growth is scattered over
uplands in an interstitial manner among other grasses.

Flowers: The spikelets are borne on simple racemes, from one side
of the rachis. It is from this arrangement of spikelets that the
plant takes its name "Side-oats."

Leaves: The leaf blades are flat, up to one cm wide, and have dead
curly tips. The dead tip is about ¼ to ⅓ the length of the blade.
The leaves often have dark pustule-looking marks. Along both the
margins of the leaves are hairs which have a bulbous gland at
their base. Magnification helps in seeing this feature.

Use or Importance: Side-oats Grama is a palatable and nutritious
grass. It increases under moderate to heavy use.

Habitat: Side-oats Grama occupies all manner of upland sites from
lower slopes to chiefly the brow of the hill or the breaks near the
crest. It may occupy deep or shallow soil.

Range: This species ranges widely over the grasslands east of the
Rocky Mountains. It is more common in Mixed Prairie than in
True Prairie, especially among the tall grasses where it does not
endure the shading so well.

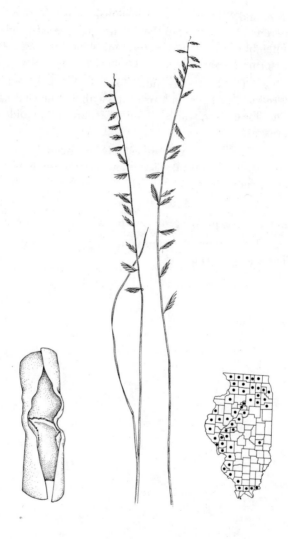

FALSE BONESET
(*Brickellia eupatorioides* (L.) Shinners)

Season and Stature: The False Boneset is a native, warm-season perennial belonging to the Compositae, or aster family. It attains a height of nearly one meter, and blooms during the Fall aspect. It formerly was known as *Kuhnia eupatorioides* L.

Flowers: The heads are numerous, peduncled, and loosely clustered in a terminal inflorescence with a somewhat flattened look. The flowers are whitish. The heads are all discoid, with no rays present.

Leaves: The leaves are alternately arranged on the stems. The leaves are linear-lanceolate, acute at the apex, narrowed to the base, short-petioled or sessile, and sparingly toothed.

Use or Importance: Little use has been attributed to this plant.

Habitat: This species grows in dry woods and prairies.

Range: False Boneset ranges from New Jersey to Montana, south to Texas and Florida.

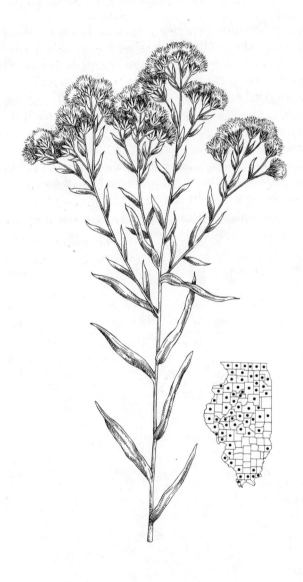

BLUE HEARTS
(*Buchnera americana* L.)

Season and Stature: Blue Hearts is a native, warm-season perennial herb belonging to the family Scrophulariaceae, the figwort family. It attains a height of 30 to 75 cm. It blooms during the Summer aspect.

Flowers: The inflorescence is a spike. The flowers are light to medium purple in color. They are nearly regular, about 1 cm long and nearly as broad.

Leaves: The leaves are opposite. The lower leaves are obovate to oblong and obtuse; the middle leaves are oblong-lanceolate, dentate, and narrowed to the sessile base; the upper leaves are linear-lanceolate and entire or nearly so.

Use or Importance: Although there is no particular importance for this plant, it adds a lovely color to the prairie landscape during the summer.

Habitat: In Illinois, this species is found mostly in hill prairies. It is not common.

Range: Blue Hearts occurs in sandy, gravelly, or dry loess soil over the eastern half of the United States, including the True Prairie area.

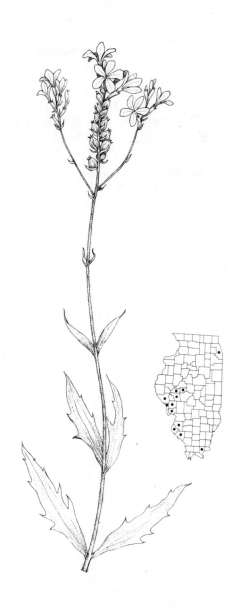

INDIAN PLANTAIN
(*Cacalia tuberosa* Nutt.)

Season and Stature: The Indian Plantain is a native, warm-season perennial belonging to the Compositae, or aster family. It attains a height of 1-2 meters and blooms during the Summer aspect.

Flowers: The heads are very numerous in a compound inflorescence. Each head is about 3 mm broad and cream-colored.

Leaves: The basal leaves are oval, ovate, or ovate-lanceolate, usually entire, narrowed at the base, petioled, and 5- to 9-veined. The upper leaves are ovate to oblong and sessile or on short petioles. The upper leaves are sometimes toothed toward the apex.

Use or Importance: The Indian Plantain has a fleshy tuber which is reported to be edible.

Habitat: This species occurs in wet prairies and in moist fields.

Range: The range of this species is from Minnesota south to Alabama and Texas.

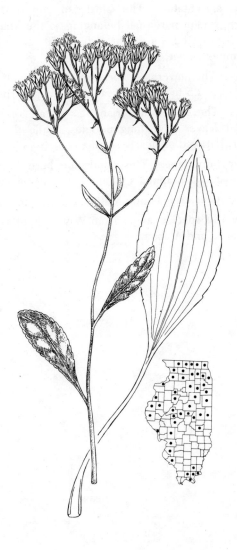

CLUSTERED POPPY MALLOW
(*Callirhoe triangulata* (Leavenw.) Gray)

Season and Stature: The Clustered Poppy Mallow is a native, warm-season perennial belonging to the Malvaceae, or mallow family. It attains a height of 35 to 70 cm. It blooms during the Summer aspect, from June to August.

Flowers: The flowers are borne in terminal panicled clusters. Each flower is 2.5 to 5.0 cm broad, and deep purple.

Leaves: The leaves are triangular-hastate or spear-shaped. The lower leaves have long petioles, while the upper leaves are short-petioled or nearly sessile.

Use or Importance: This handsome herb is a decreaser under grazing and disappears when grazing is uncontrolled.

Habitat: Clustered Poppy Mallow is found in sandy habitats.

Range: This species ranges from Wisconsin to Texas, east to North Carolina and Alabama.

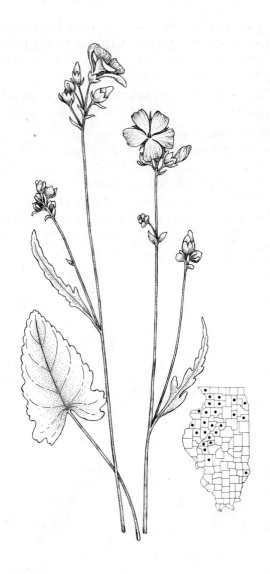

WILD HYACINTH
(*Camassia scilloides* (Raf.) Cory)

Season and Stature: Wild Hyacinth is a native, cool-season perennial belonging to the Liliaceae, or lily family. It attains a height up to 60 cm. It flowers during the Spring aspect.

Flowers: There are about 10 to 12 or more flowers at the ends of slender flower stalks. The perianth has six members which are pale blue. They are about 20 mm long. There are six stamens.

Leaves: All leaves of the plant are basal. The smooth leaves are up to 30 cm long and about 1.5 cm wide.

Use or Importance: In growing from bulbs, the plants lend themselves to transplanting into gardens.

Habitat: Wild Hyacinth occurs in prairies and in open woods.

Range: The range of the Wild Hyacinth is from Pennsylvania to Michigan, south to Texas to Georgia.

MEAD'S SEDGE
(Carex meadii Dew.)

Season and Stature: Mead's Sedge is a native species which attains a height of about 50 cm. It flowers during the Spring and early Summer aspects. It belongs to the Cyperaceae, or sedge family.

Flowers: The staminate spike is borne on a long stalk and is densely crowded with pollen-producing flowers. The 1-3 oblong-cylindric pistillate spikes are up to 2 cm long and up to 5 mm across.

Leaves: The leaves of the sedge are flat and measure from 3-5 mm across. They are smooth.

Use or Importance: This sedge has minimal importance as a forage plant.

Habitat: Mead's Sedge grows in moist soil or prairies and meadows throughout most of Illinois.

Range: The range of this plant is from southern Ontario to Saskatchewan, south to Texas and Georgia.

PENN SEDGE
(*Carex pensylvanica* Lam.)

Season and Stature: Penn Sedge grows in tufts up to 30 cm tall. It is a native sedge which blooms during the Spring aspect. It belongs to the Cyperaceae, or sedge, family.

Flowers: The staminate spike is reddish-brown and up to 2 cm long. It is usually borne on a short stalk. The 1-4 ovoid pistillate spikes are up to 1.2 cm long and sessile or on very short stalks.

Leaves: Leaves of the Penn Sedge are very slender, reaching a width of only 3 mm.

Use or Importance: To a small extent, this sedge is used for forage.

Habitat: Penn Sedge grows in dry soil of both prairies and woodlands.

Range: This sedge ranges from Quebec to North Dakota, south to Iowa, Illinois, Tennessee, and North Carolina.

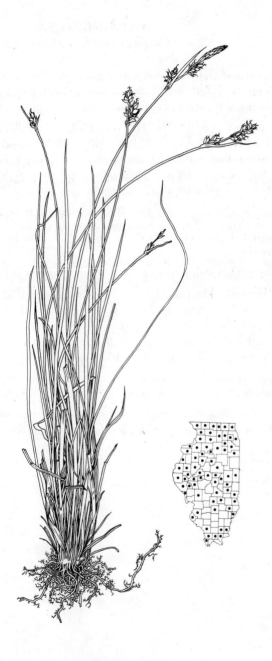

PARTRIDGE PEA
(*Cassia fasciculata* Michx.)

Season and Stature: This native plant is an annual and is one of a very small number of annual species found in prairie vegetation. It is a member of the Leguminosae, or legume family. It flowers during the Summer aspect and well into Autumn. The height of the Partridge Pea is up to 60 cm or more.

Flowers: The showy yellow flowers are 2.5 to 3.5 cm broad. The flowers are not the typical pea-shape of most legumes, but are almost symmetrical in appearance.

Leaves: The leaves are pinnately compound with from 12-30 leaflets. The leaflets are linear to narrowly oblong and asymmetrical at the base.

Use or Importance: Partridge Pea is very palatable to livestock. It does not bulk high as a forage source because it is an annual. In the south, the plant provides nectar to bees, and is a good honey plant. The Partridge Pea tends to grow in infertile places where other plants are few, and it improves the soil by its nitrogen-fixing habit. It can be successfully grown from seed by scarification. It is reported to be a good food source for upland birds.

Habitat: Partridge Pea occurs in most sandy open soils. It is particularly common along roads and in old fields.

Range: This species ranges over most of the eastern United States, from Massachusetts and Florida to South Dakota and Texas.

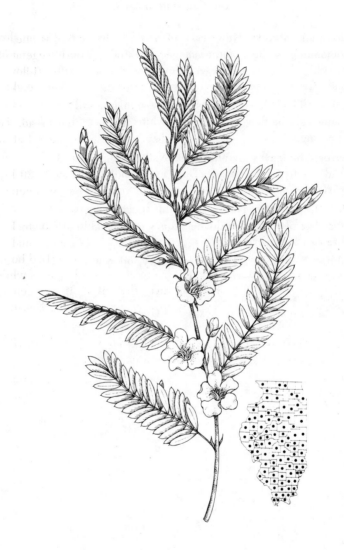

NEW JERSEY TEA
(*Ceanothus americanus* L.)

Season and Stature: New Jersey Tea is a native, cool-season shrub belonging to the Rhamnaceae, or buckthorn, family. It attains a height of about one meter. New Jersey Tea flowers during the late Spring aspect.

Flowers: The flowers are borne in terminal or axillary corymbs or panicles. The flowers, which are white, are on pedicels less than 1 cm long.

Leaves: The leaves are alternate, ovate to oblong, up to 6 cm long, and up to 3 cm broad. They are usually hairy on the lower surface.

Use or Importance: The leaves of this species may be used to brew a tea. The plant is grazed when young and tends to disappear when prairies are overgrazed.

Habitat: New Jersey Tea occurs in dry, open woods, rocky slopes, and prairie borders.

Range: This species is found across southern Canada from Quebec to Manitoba, south to Texas and Georgia.

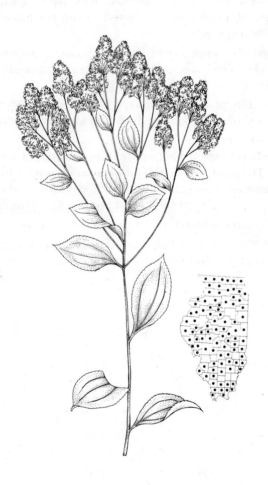

WATER HEMLOCK
(*Cicuta maculata* L.)

Season and Stature: The Water Hemlock is a native, warm-season perennial belonging to the Umbelliferae, or parsley family. It attains a height up to 1.5 meters. It flowers during the Summer aspect.

Flowers: The small white flowers are borne in compound, many rayed umbels. Each flower has five sepals, five petals, and five stamens.

Leaves: The pinnately compound leaves are alternately arranged on stout, hollow stems. The leaflets are coarsely toothed.

Use or Importance: The Water Hemlock is poisonous to all warm-blooded animals. The roots and rootstocks are most poisonous. Only a small part of the rootstock is enough to cause death to humans. The poisonous material is cicutoxin, and the symptoms of poisoning are frothing, tremoring, and convulsion.

Habitat: This species grows in moist situations, including wet prairies.

Range: Water Hemlock occurs over the entire eastern half of the United States.

FALSE TOADFLAX
(*Comandra richardsiana* Fern.)

Season and Stature: The False Toadflax is a warm-season, native herb in the Santalaceae, or sandalwood family. It attains a height of 10 to 15 cm, and blooms from May to August.

Flowers: The flowers are creamy white, with 4 stamens which are opposite the perianth lobes. There are no petals, but the sepals are whitish and petal-like. The cymes are several-flowered, becoming corymbose at the summit of the plant. The flowers are axillary, with short pedicels.

Leaves: The leaves are numerous, ascending, alternate on the stem, oblong or oblong-lanceolate, acute at each end, and sessile.

Use or Importance: This small plant lives as a partial parasite on the roots of various trees.

Habitat: In Illinois, this plant is found in dry prairies or sometimes in sparse woods. It is occasional.

Range: The False Toadflax is found over the areas of True and Mixed Prairie.

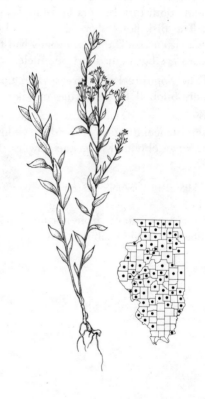

STIFF TICKSEED
(Coreopsis palmata Nutt.)*

Season and Stature: The Stiff Tickseed is a native, warm-season perennial belonging to the Compositae, or aster family. It attains a height of up to 90 cm and flowers during the Summer aspect.

Flowers: The flowers are bright and deep yellow, measuring 2.5 to 5 cm broad. Both disk flowers and ray flowers are present in the heads. The disk flowers are perfect and fertile, while the ray flowers are neutral. The rays are mostly 3-toothed at the tip. The few heads are borne on short peduncles.

Leaves: The opposite leaves are sessile, up to 7.5 cm long, and palmately 3-lobed to about the middle. The lobes are linear-oblong.

Use or Importance: Because of the deep yellow color of the petals, a dye has been obtained from the flowers. It is most effective on wool.

Habitat: The Stiff Tickseed is found on dry prairies and in open woods.

Range: This species ranges from northern Indiana and Wisconsin to Manitoba, south to Oklahoma and southern Illinois.

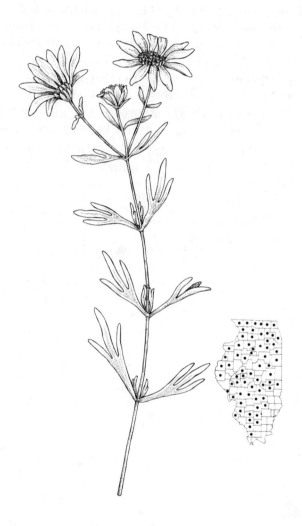

SHOOTING-STAR
(*Dodecatheon meadia* L.)

Season and Stature: The Shooting-star is a native, cool-season perennial belonging to the Primulaceae, or primrose family. It attains a height up to 60 cm and blooms during the Spring aspect.

Flowers: The flowers, which are few to several in umbels, are purplish to usually pink or whitish. The calyx is deeply 5-lobed, and the petals are 5, with reflexed lobes.

Leaves: The leaves are basal, oblanceolate, narrowed into margined petioles, pale green, 7 to 20 cm long, 1.5 to 6 cm wide.

Use or Importance: Shooting-star is a handsome species which has been grown successfully in gardens.

Habitat: This species occurs in prairies, on moist slopes, and on rocky hillsides.

Range: Shooting-star occurs from Pennsylvania to Georgia, west to Wisconsin and Texas.

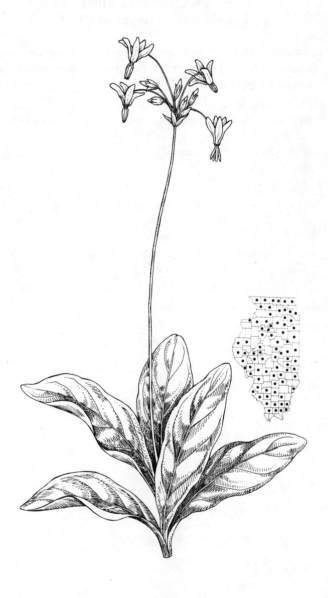

PALE PRAIRIE CONEFLOWER
(*Echinacea pallida* (Nutt.) Nutt.)

Season and Stature: The Pale Prairie Coneflower is one of the handsomest of the prairie herbs. It is a native, warm-season perennial growing up to 60 cm tall. It is a member of the Compositae, or aster family.

Flowers: In total diameter each head is about 4 cm. The central disk is about 2.5 cm. The rays are pinkish and extend slightly downward. After the rays drop off, the seed head turns a dark brown color.

Leaves: The plant produces a few ovate-lanceolate leaves at ground level. These basal leaves are up to 20 cm long and 3 to 4 cm broad. The leaves are harshly pubescent and have about 3 prominent veins. Smaller leaves extend up the stems.

Use or Importance: Besides its natural beauty and adaptability as a garden plant, this species is grazed and contributes toward roughage in livestock diet. It decreases under grazing.

Habitat: This species occurs in prairies.

Range: The range of the Pale Prairie Coneflower is from Michigan to Nebraska, south to Texas and Alabama.

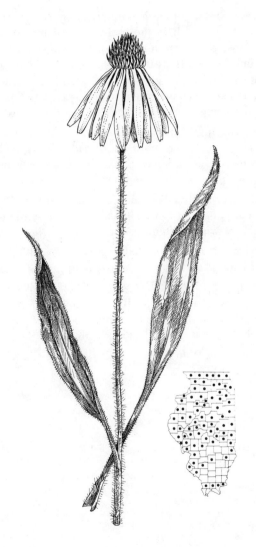

NODDING WILD RYE
(*Elymus canadensis* L.)

Season and Stature: This moderately tall grass, usually slightly over one meter, is fifth in the moisture gradient of the lowland. It would also rank fifth in importance or abundance among the five lowland dominants. It is a cool-season, perennial grass forming a weak sod. It begins growth in March or April and matures by July. It may become green at the base of the plant and renew growth during the Fall aspect. It is a winter-hardy plant.

Flowers: The spikes are dense, usually curving or nodding, 10 to 25 cm long, and 2 or more cm broad. The spikelets are 2- to 7-flowered. The lemmas usually have long curving awns which give the spikes a bushy look.

Leaves: Green early season and fall season growth is expected. The leaves are one cm or more in width, and clasp the culm by means of auricles which extend part way around the culm.

Use or Importance: The Nodding Wild Rye is highly palatable. Because of its early growth, it is sought by all classes of livestock. It is a decreaser in prairies which are grazed too short, too early.

Habitat: The Nodding Wild Rye is a lowland dominant found in True Prairie in the transition from lowland to upland. Roadsides and cinder banks along railroads also provide suitable habitat.

Range: Nodding Wild Rye is widely distributed throughout most of the United States.

RATTLESNAKE MASTER
(*Eryngium yuccifolium* Michx.)

Season and Stature: This member of the Umbelliferae, or parsley family, is a native, warm-season perennial which grows to a height of one meter or more. It flowers during the Summer aspect.

Flowers: The flowers are borne in thistle-like, spherical heads up to 2.5 cm in diameter. The flowers are small, with 5 sepals, 5 petals, and 5 stamens. The ovary is inferior.

Leaves: The leaves of the Rattlesnake Master are stiffish, bayonet-shaped with teeth along the margins, and look much like those of yucca, from which its Latin name is derived.

Use or Importance: New growth of Rattlesnake Master is palatable and nutritious. It is readily grazed and thus behaves as a decreaser. The common name indicates the early settlers thought the plant had use in treatment of rattlesnake bite. This was unfounded. The plant can be dried and used in indoor winter decorations.

Habitat: This species occurs in both prairies and woods.

Range: Rattlesnake Master ranges from New Jersey to Minnesota, south to Texas and Florida.

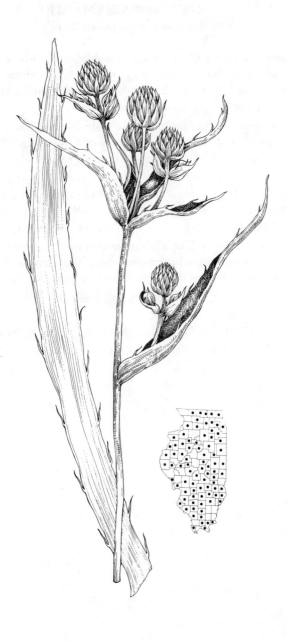

FLAT-TOPPED SPURGE
(*Euphorbia corollata* L.)

Season and Stature: The Flat-topped Spurge is a native, warm-season perennial herb belonging to the Euphorbiaceae, or spurge family. It attains a height up to about one meter. This species blooms during the Summer aspect.

Flowers: Several white flowers are arranged in a cymosely branched inflorescence which spreads to a width of 15 to 20 cm. The flowers are without petals, but there are five white petal-like appendages. The ovary is 3-lobed.

Leaves: The leaves are linear-oblong, 1 to 2 cm long, entire, short-petioled or sessile. The leaves at the base of the inflorescence are several in a whorl. The entire plant contains milky sap.

Use or Importance: The Flat-topped Spurge is one of the top ranking upland herbs of the True Prairie in abundance. It tends to disappear from prairies which are too heavily grazed.

Habitat: This species is common in prairies, dry woods, fields, and along roads.

Range: The range of the Flat-topped Spurge is from New York to Minnesota, south to Florida and Texas.

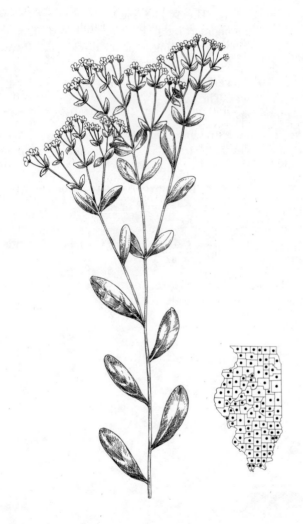

WILD STRAWBERRY
(*Fragaria virginiana* Duchesne)

Season and Stature: The Wild Strawberry is a native, cool-season perennial belonging to the Rosaceae, or rose family. It is a low-growing herb, flowering at about the level of its own leaves which are 0.5 to 15 cm high.

Flowers: The flowering stalks are about equal to or slightly shorter than the leaves. The petals are five and white, while the stamens are numerous.

Leaves: The Wild Strawberry has dark green, 3-parted leaves which are on petioles 0.5 to 15 cm long. The leaflets are short stalked or sessile, oval to obovate, and serrate.

Use or Importance: Wild Strawberries are edible, but small.

Habitat: Wild Strawberry is found in prairies, fields, and along the borders of woods.

Range: This species occurs from eastern Canada to Georgia, west to Minnesota and Oklahoma.

STIFF MARSH BEDSTRAW
(*Galium tinctorium* L.)

Season and Stature: The Stiff Marsh Bedstraw is a native, warm-season perennial belonging to the Rubiaceae, or madder family. It attains a height of 15 to 30 cm, and blooms during the early Summer aspect.

Flowers: The flowers are in terminal clusters of 2 to 3. The pedicels are slender and bear flowers which are white, 1 to 2 mm broad, and 4-parted. The ovary is inferior.

Leaves: The leaves are in clusters of 4, 5, or 6 along the square stems. The leaves are linear to lanceolate, broadest below the middle, tapered at each end.

Use or Importance: This plant is called bedstraw from the fact that it and other species of the genus were used as stuffing for mattresses or bed ticking in early days. It has also been mixed with rennet in preparation of cheese.

Habitat: Stiff Marsh Bedstraw grows in many moist habitats including wet prairies.

Range: This species ranges across the eastern half of Canada, south to Texas, Illinois, and South Carolina.

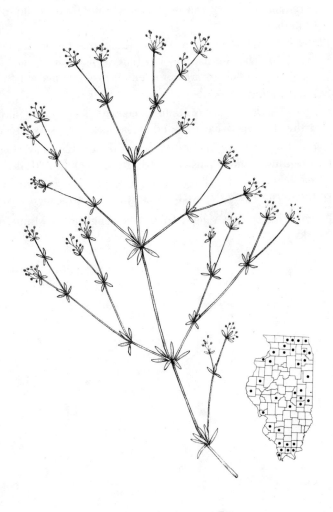

CLOSED GENTIAN
(Gentiana andrewsii Griseb.)

Season and Stature: The Closed Gentian is a native, warm-season perennial which may grow to a height of 60 cm. It flowers from August to October.

Flowers: As the common name indicates, the flowers are closed or nearly so. The corolla, which is blue or pale bluish, is 2.5 to 3.5 cm long. The flowers are borne either in a terminal cluster of 2 to 4 or in upper axils where there may be 1 to 2.

Leaves: The leaves are ovate to lanceolate, 3- to 7-nerved, pointed at the tip, somewhat rounded at the base, and sessile.

Use or Importance: The bitter juice of the gentians have long been valued as a tonic. This plant has sometimes been called "ague-weed."

Habitat: The Closed Gentian grows in damp prairies.

Range: This species ranges from New England to Minnesota and Arkansas.

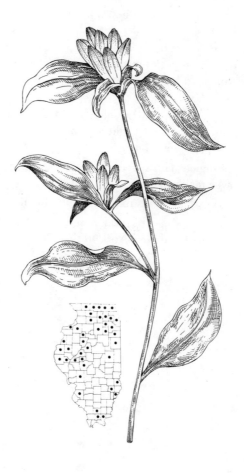

DOWNY GENTIAN
(*Gentiana puberulenta* Pringle)

Season and Stature: The late blooming gentian of the Gentianaceae family is a native, warm-season or fall-blooming perennial herb. It attains a height of 20 to 40 cm or more, and blooms from August to October, and is much overtopped by the grasses at this time.

Flowers: The flowers are deep blue, tubular, of five petals, 5 stamens, and a superior ovary. The flowers are sessile or nearly so in the upper axils of the leaves. Flowers are rarely solitary and terminal.

Leaves: The stems are usually solitary with lanceolate upper leaves, and the lower leaves are slightly oblong. The leaves are narrowed at the base, and are from 2.5 to 7.5 cm long.

Use or Importance: This species decreases under grazing. The deep blue flower makes it especially attractive.

Habitat: Downy Gentian is found in most Illinois dry prairie types.

Range: This species occurs from Kansas and North Dakota in the west to Georgia and New York in the east.

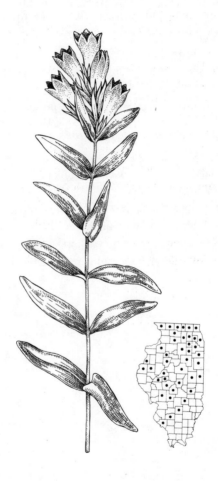

PRAIRIE-SMOKE
(Geum triflorum Pursh)

Season and Stature: Prairie-smoke is a native cool-season plant belonging to the family Rosaceae. It attains a height of 15 to 45 cm, and blooms from May through June, or during the late Spring aspect.

Flowers: Three flowers are borne at the summit of a simple scape. Flowers are up to 1 cm broad, showy, and purple. The fruits are plumose.

Leaves: The basal leaves are tufted, petioled, interruptedly pinnate (small leaflets interspersed among the numerous larger leaflets). The stems are softly hairy.

Use or Importance: Prairie-smoke is an early-blooming species of unusual appearance. Because of its plumose fruits, it is also called "old man's whiskers."

Habitat: Prairie-smoke is found on high gravel or morainal areas and also on calcareous soils in the northern part of the state.

Range: This plant shows its northern affinity by ranging from Newfoundland and Labrador to British Columbia, Illinois, Iowa, and North Dakota.

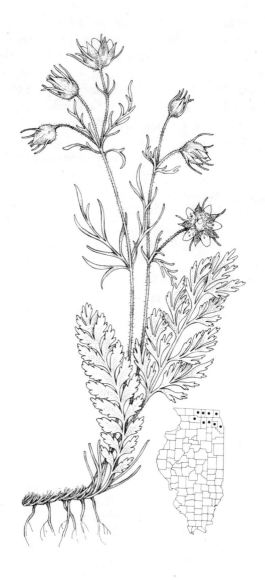

SAWTOOTH SUNFLOWER
(*Helianthus grosseserratus* Martens)

Season and Stature: The Sawtooth Sunflower is a native, warm-season perennial herb belonging to the family Compositae. It attains a height of up to 2.5 meters, and flowers during the Fall aspect.

Flowers: The ray flowers are neutral; the disk flowers are perfect and fertile. The heads are numerous, 3 to 7 cm broad, with 10 to 20 deep yellow rays. The disk is yellowish.

Leaves: The leaves are long-lanceolate, with slender petioles. The upper leaves are alternate, the lower ones opposite. Leaves are sharply serrate, rough above, hairy beneath, 10 to 20 cm long, up to 2.5 cm wide.

Use or Importance: The presence of this species was used as an indicator of good corn land.

Habitat: In Illinois, this species occurs in all parts of the state and probably in every prairie type which provides a moist lowland habitat.

Range: Sawtooth Sunflower occurs in the eastern United States, especially in the True Prairie area. This species accompanies tall grasses in the prairies.

HAIRY SUNFLOWER
(*Helianthus mollis* Lam.)

Season and Stature: Hairy Sunflower is a warm-season, mid-sized perennial belonging to the Compositae, or aster family. It reaches a height of about one meter. It flowers during the Summer and Fall aspects.

Flowers: The flower heads are 5 to 6 cm broad and bear several yellow rays around a yellow disk.

Leaves: The sessile leaves are borne in opposite arrangement on the stem. The leaves are densely hairy and rough to the touch.

Use or Importance: Hairy Sunflower is highly nutritious and palatable and is relished by grazing animals. For this reason, it is a plant which decreases under grazing.

Habitat: This species grows in dry soils in prairies and woods.

Range: The Hairy Sunflower ranges from Michigan to Iowa, south to Texas and Georgia.

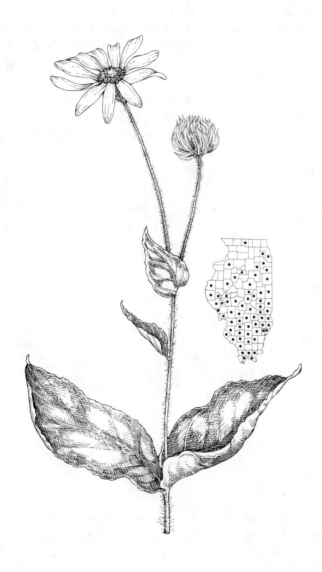

STIFF SUNFLOWER
(*Helianthus rigidus* (Cass.) Desf.)

Season and Stature: The Stiff Sunflower is a warm-season perennial in the Compositae, or aster family. It attains a height up to 1 meter, and blooms during the late Summer and Fall aspects.

Flowers: The rays of the Stiff Sunflower are over 1 cm long and surround the red or purple disk.

Leaves: The leaves are oppositely arranged, lanceolate to ovate, mostly toothed, rough to the touch on both surfaces.

Use or Importance: The Stiff Sunflower is palatable to grazing animals and decreases under grazing pressure.

Habitat: The Stiff Sunflower occurs in dry prairies.

Range: This species ranges from New York and Georgia into the western states. It has been known in the past as *H. laetifolrus.*

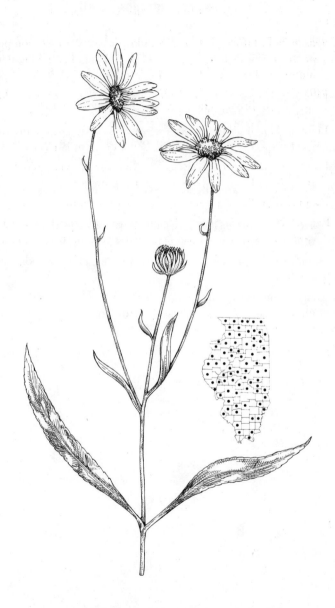

JERUSALEM ARTICHOKE
(*Helianthus tuberosus* L.)

Season and Stature: The Jerusalem Artichoke is a native, warm-season perennial in the Compositae, or aster family. The plant attains a height up to 3 meters. It blooms during the Fall aspect.

Flowers: There are several yellow heads on each plant, measuring up to 8 cm broad. The rays, which number from 12 to 20, and the disk are yellow.

Leaves: The leaves are ovate, ovate-oblong, or ovate-lanceolate, 3-veined, narrowed at the base, petiolate, rough to the touch, and serrate. They are up to 20 cm long and up to 7 cm wide. The upper leaves are alternate, while the lower ones are generally opposite.

Use or Importance: The Jerusalem Artichoke has thickened, starchy tubers which are edible. The plant is adaptable to cultivation.

Habitat: This species grows in wet prairies, damp woods, and along roads.

Range: The natural range of this species is thought to be from Ontario and Saskatchewan, south to Kansas, Arkansas, and Georgia.

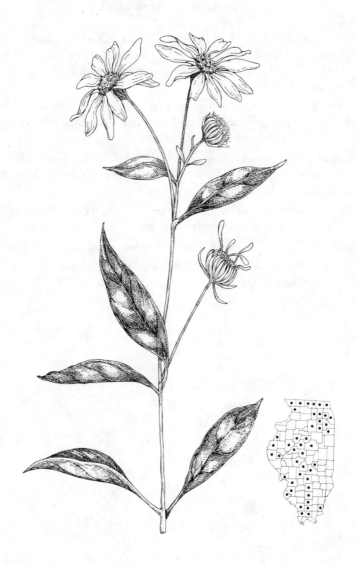

FALSE SUNFLOWER
(*Heliopsis helianthoides* L.)

Season and Stature: The False Sunflower is a native, warm-season perennial herb belonging to the Compositae, or aster family. It attains a height of a meter or more and blooms during the Fall aspect.

Flowers: The heads are long peduncled, and are 3 to 6 cm broad. The yellow disk flowers bear both stamens and pistils, while the yellow ray flowers have only pistils.

Leaves: The leaves are opposite, petioled, ovate-lanceolate, acuminate at the tip, sharply toothed, somewhat rough on both surfaces, 7 to 15 cm long, 2.5 to 6 cm wide.

Use or Importance: The plant is palatable when grazed and tends to decrease in prairies which are grazed.

Habitat: False Sunflower occurs in open woods and dry prairies.

Range: This species ranges from New York to Minnesota, south to New Mexico, Arkansas, and North Carolina.

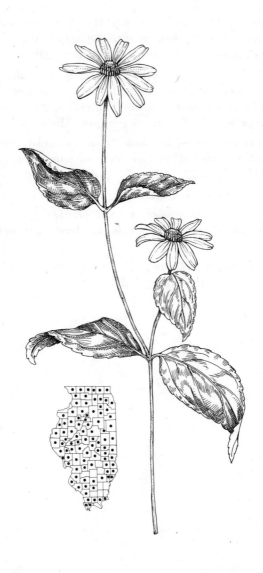

ROUGH HEUCHERA OR ALUMROOT
(*Heuchera richardsonii* R. Br.)

Season and Stature: The Rough Heuchera is a native cool-season perennial species belonging to the family Saxifragaceae. It attains a height of over 60 cm and flowers during the late Spring aspect.

Flowers: The inflorescence is narrowly paniculate. The calyx is cup-shaped and asymmetrical, 3 to 5 mm long. The petals are spatulate and longer than the calyx; the stamens extend beyond the petals. The flower color is greenish-cream.

Leaves: The leaves are basal, ovate-orbicular, and have 5 to 9 shallow, rounded, coarsely toothed lobes. The stems are hairy.

Use or Importance: There is little known importance for this obscurely flowered species.

Habitat: Rough Heuchera grows in prairies, roadsides, and rights-of-way as a relict of the prairie. In Illinois, it occurs in a variety of prairie types.

Range: This species grows in the True Prairie region and eastward, as well as in the Mixed Prairie to the west.

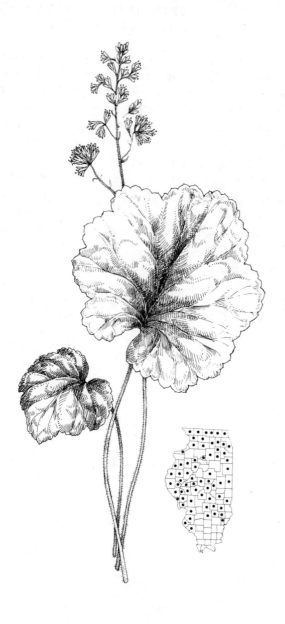

LITTLE WILD BARLEY
(*Hordeum pusillum* Nutt.)

Season and Stature: A native, weedy, annual species of grass is the Little Wild Barley. It is a cool-season, short-lived species which attains a height up to 30 cm or more. It flowers and produces fruit during the Spring aspect and early Summer aspect.

Flowers: The spikes are up to 6-8 cm in length and are dense and erect. Spikelets are 3 at each joint and are awned.

Leaves: The root system is shallow. The leaf blades are up to 7 cm long, flat, and somewhat rough on the upper surface.

Use or Importance: Limited grazing is about the only use made of Little Wild Barley, and this occurs during Spring. The plant serves as an indicator of overgrazed prairie or pasture.

Habitat: Little Wild Barley is most often found in disturbed areas within prairie. The species occupies a wide variety of soils.

Range: The Little Wild Barley is found over much of the United States. Most annuals have a way of fitting into a wide variety of environmental circumstances and conditions.

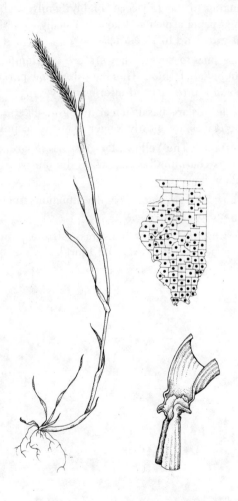

YELLOW STAR-GRASS
(*Hypoxis hirsuta* (L.) Coville)

Season and Stature: The Yellow Star-grass is a native, short perennial belonging to the Liliaceae, or lily family. It begins growth during the Spring aspect and flowers usually into May and June. The plant grows up to 15 cm tall.

Flowers: The one to several flowers are on slender scapes in a simple, umbellate fashion. There are six yellow perianth parts, six stamens, and a three-parted inferior ovary.

Leaves: The leaves are basal, linear and grass-like, and somewhat hairy. The leaves are mostly longer than the scapes.

Use or Importance: The Yellow Star-grass has no great importance, although it is charming because of its diminutive stature and its bright yellow flowers.

Habitat: Yellow Star-grass occurs in dry situations, including woods, blufftops, and prairies.

Range: The range for Yellow Star-grass is from New England to North Dakota, south to Texas and Florida.

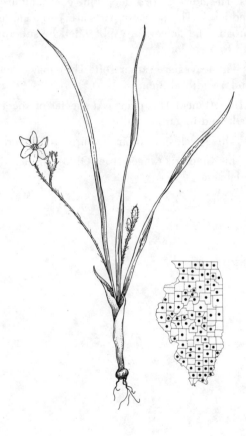

BLUE IRIS
(*Iris brevicaulis* Raf.)

Season and Stature: This Blue Iris is a cool-season, native perennial in the Iridaceae, or iris family. It attains a height of 20 to 40 cm and blooms during the Spring aspect.

Flowers: The flowers are a deep blue color and are borne near the ground level. The perianth parts are 7 to 9 cm long and 2.5 to 3 cm broad. The flowers are subtended by subequal bracts which are up to 5 cm long.

Leaves: The leaves are rather soft. They may reach a length of 60 cm and a width of 3 cm.

Use or Importance: This plant is a species of special beauty and is well adapted to garden culture.

Habitat: This species occurs in swampy woods and in wet prairies.

Range: This Blue Iris ranges from Ohio to Kansas, south to Texas and Alabama.

BLUE IRIS
(*Iris shrevei* Small)

Season and Stature: The Blue Iris, or Wild Flag, is a native perennial reaching a height of one meter. It flowers during May and June. It belongs to the Iridaceae, or iris family.

Flowers: The blue flowers are up to 8 cm broad and have three stamens. There is an inferior ovary.

Leaves: The leaves are sword-shaped and up to one meter long and up to 3 cm broad.

Use or Importance: The beauty of this species is such that the plant is sometimes transplanted into flower gardens.

Habitat: Blue Iris grows in a variety of wet situations, including prairies.

Range: The range of this species is from Ontario to Minnesota, south to Texas and Alabama.

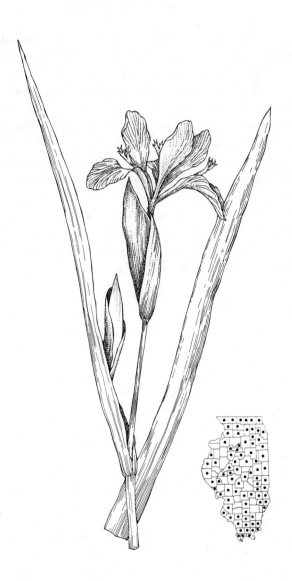

PATH RUSH
(*Juncus tenuis* Willd.)

Season and Stature: Path Rush is a native cool-season plant having a tufted growth and attaining a height up to 90 cm.

Flowers: The inflorescence is usually exceeded by an elongated bract. The flowers are greenish-brown and up to 3 mm long. There are six stamens.

Leaves: The Path Rush has basal leaves which are about half the length of the culms. The leaves are about 1 mm wide.

Use or Importance: This species is called Path Rush because it grows on pathways. It may be used to indicate both a moist soil and a compacted soil.

Habitat: This species grows in moist or dry soil, compacted soil in pathways, open fields, and in prairies.

Range: The Path Rush grows throughout North America and has spread to several parts of the World.

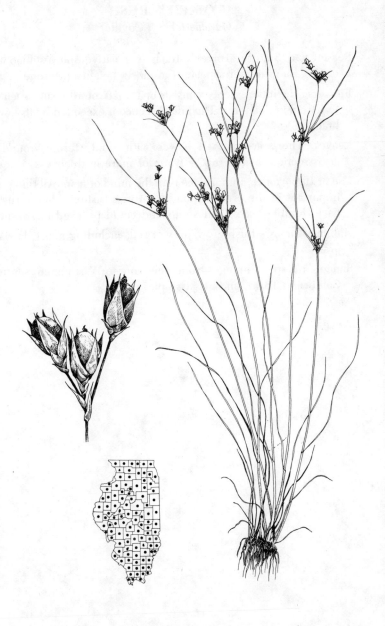

TORREY'S RUSH
(*Juncus torreyi* Coville)

Season and Stature: Torrey's Rush is a native species blooming during the Summer aspect. It attains a height up to one meter.

Flowers: The inflorescence consists of 1 to 20 round heads, each 0.5 to 1.0 cm in diameter. The inflorescence is exceeded by its lowest bract.

Leaves: There are 1 to 4 leaves with stout, terete (round in cross-section) blades, up to 1 mm or more in thickness.

Use or Importance: Importance is in the mind of man. All things are important in the organization of nature's systems. Many rushes have durable leaves and stems and could be used in basketry.

Habitat: Torrey's Rush grows in wet soil, including moist, lowland prairies.

Range: This species ranges from New York to Washington, south to California, Texas, and Mississippi.

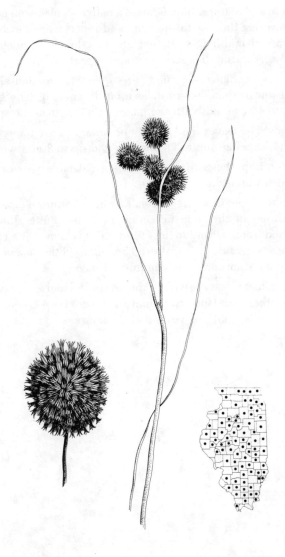

JUNE GRASS
(*Koeleria macrantha* (Ledeb.) Spreng.)

Season and Stature: June Grass is a native, cool-season perennial. At flowering time, with the culm and inflorescence included, it is a grass of mid-height. It thus attains a height of about 60 cm. It flowers during the early Summer aspect.

Flowers: At flowering time, the spikelets are densely borne in narrow or spike-like panicles up to 12 cm long. The spikelets are 2- to 4-flowered, with the glumes shorter than the spikelets.

Leaves: The leaves tend to twist or spiral and are unevenly veined. The leaves are up to 20 cm long and up to 3 mm wide.

Use or Importance: June Grass is a palatable species which decreases under heavy grazing of the prairies.

Habitat: June Grass is a small bunch or tufted species whose position in the moisture gradient is indefinite. June Grass is found from lowland to driest hilltop. It is known as an insterstitial species because it is scattered among the other major dominants and does not form a community of its own.

Range: June Grass is a widely spread species and is found in most all the other grassland associations. It ranges from Quebec to British Columbia, south to Texas and Delaware.

BUSH LESPEDEZA
(*Lespedeza capitata* Michx.)

Season and Stature: Bush Lespedeza is a native, warm-season perennial of the Leguminosae, or legume family. It attains a height of one meter or more. It flowers during the late Summer or early Fall aspect.

Flowers: The small pea-shaped flowers are borne in a roundish head-like inflorescence which turns a dark brown at maturity. The "heads" are up to 3 cm broad.

Leaves: The leaves are divided into three leaflets. The leaflets are eliptical and sometimes covered with fine, silvery hairs.

Use or Importance: Bush Lespedeza is excellent forage and behaves as a decreaser under heavy grazing. The seeds of this species, as with many of the lespedezas, provide excellent food for game birds.

Habitat: Bush Lespedeza grows in dry soil of prairies and woods.

Range: This species ranges from New England to Minnesota, south to Texas and Florida.

VIRGINIA LESPEDEZA
(*Lespedeza virginica* (L.) Britt.)

Season and Stature: This species of Lespedeza is a native, warm-season plant. It has slender stems which grow erect to a height of 1 meter. Flowering is during August and September.

Flowers: The flowers appear in small clusters on the upper half of the plant. They are small and pinkish colored.

Leaves: The leaves are compound with three linear or narrowly oblong leaflets. The leaflets are up to 4 cm long and up to 7 mm broad.

Use or Importance: The Virginia Lespedeza is palatable and nutritious and readily grazed. It decreases under heavy grazing. Abundant seeds are produced and supply important food to upland game birds. The seeds germinate without problems, and it is therefore not too difficult to establish the species in new locations.

Habitat: The species is tolerant of shade and grows well on clay-loam soils. It is found in dry open woods as well as the prairies.

Range: Virginia Lespedeza ranges from New Hampshire to Wisconsin and Kansas, south to Texas and Florida.

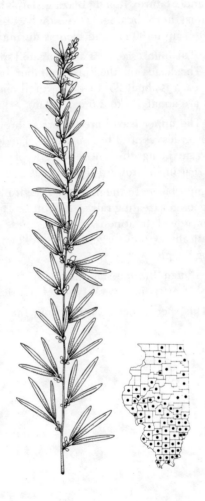

ROUGH BLAZING-STAR
(*Liatris aspera* Michx.)

Season and Stature: Rough Blazing-star is a native, warm-season perennial herb belonging to family Compositae. It attains a height of up to 90 cm and blooms during the Fall aspect.

Flowers: The inflorescence is an elongated spike, up to nearly 60 cm long. The heads on the spike number from 20 to over 100 or more; each is about 25- to 40-flowered, and purple in color. The heads are about 1.5 to 2.5 cm broad.

Leaves: The upper leaves are linear, scabrous, and slightly ciliate. The lower leaves are 1 to 2 cm broad. The leaves are alternate and are borne along the entire length of the stem, diminishing somewhat in size toward the summit.

Use or Importance: In the past, the Rough Blazing-star was thought to be good for treating rattlesnake bites. The corms were used for this unproved treatment. Mainly, these plants are important aesthetically as they brighten the yellows of autumn with contrasting purple.

Habitat: Rough Blazing-star occurs in dry or sandy soil and, in Illinois, it exists in several types of prairie.

Range: This species occurs throughout the range of True Prairie.

TALL GAYFEATHER
(*Liatris pycnostachya* Michx.)

Season and Stature: Tall Gayfeather is a native, warm-season perennial belonging to the Compositae, or aster family. It is a long lived plant with roots penetrating to over fifteen feet. It attains a height of 1.5 meters.

Flowers: The flowers are borne close to the upper end of the stem in dense clusters. The rose-purple flowers are very showy.

Leaves: Short hairs exist on both the stems and leaves so that the entire plant has a stiff, harsh look. The leaves are narrow or linear and are longest at the lower end of the plant and are progressively shorter near the flowers.

Use or Importance: The Tall Gayfeather is grazed by livestock and is classed as a decreaser by range managers. The plant is normally associated with Big Bluestem, and is conspicuous at a distance. When the blossoms are collected and dried, they preserve well as an indoor decoration.

Habitat: This species grows in lowland prairies.

Range: Tall Gayfeather ranges from Wisconsin to South Dakota, south to Texas and Louisiana.

SCALY BLAZING STAR
(*Liatris squarrosa* (L.) Michx.)

Season and Stature: The Scaly Blazing Star, also known as the Colic Root, is a native, warm-season perennial herb belonging to the Compositae, or aster family. It attains a height of 15 to 60 cm and blooms during the Fall aspect.

Flowers: The heads are sessile or on short peduncles and bear from 15 to 60 flowers. The heads, which are up to 3 cm high and about half as broad, are rose-purple. The bracts at the base of each head are in 5 to 7 series, lanceolate, acuminate, and spreading.

Leaves: The leaves are narrowly linear, stiff, dotted, up to 15 cm long, and 3 to 4 mm wide. They are alternate along the stem.

Use or Importance: The common name would indicate that the root has use in treating colic, although this attribute is unverified. The Scaly Blazing Star decreases when prairies are heavily grazed.

Habitat: This species grows in dry woods and prairies.

Range: Scaly Blazing Star is found from Delaware across to Missouri, south to Alabama and Florida.

TURK'S-CAP LILY
(*Lilium michiganense* Farw.)

Season and Stature: The wild Turk's-cap Lily is a Summer aspect plant which attains a height of up to 2 meters. It grows from an underground bulb. It belongs to the Liliaceae, or lily family.

Flowers: The flowers are orange or orange-yellow with brownish-purplish spots. The flowers are from one (rarely) to several and are borne on long peduncles. The perianth segments are 5 to 10 cm long, lanceolate, and strongly recurved.

Leaves: The lanceolate leaves are smooth, tapering at both ends, 5 to 15 cm long, up to 4 cm wide, and grouped in clusters of 3 to 8.

Use or Importance: Because the flowers are handsome, the plants are sometimes taken into gardens for cultivation.

Habitat: Turk's-cap Lily grows in a variety of rather moist habitats, including prairies and woods.

Range: This species ranges from Ontario to Manitoba, south to Arkansas and Tennessee.

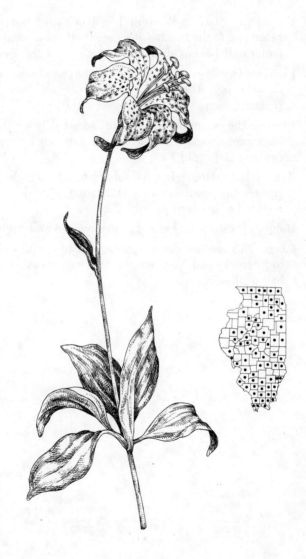

WESTERN LILY
(*Lilium philadelphicum* L.)

Season and Stature: Western Lily is a native warm-season plant belonging to the family Liliaceae. It attains a height of up to one meter and blooms during June or July of the Summer aspect.

Flowers: The flowers are orange to orange-red and very striking in their beauty. There are 1 to 5 flowers on stout pedicels. The perianth parts are purple spotted within.

Leaves: The uppermost leaves are whorled, while the lowermost leaves are alternate. The leaves are narrowly lanceolate, up to 10 cm long and up to 1 cm wide.

Use or Importance: Because of its beauty and bulb habit, this species has possibilities for cultivation in gardens, as well as in restored or artificial prairies.

Habitat: Western Lily grows in dry prairies and dry woodlands.

Range: This species occurs from Quebec to British Columbia, south to Kentucky and New Mexico. It is only occasional in the upper half of Illinois.

HOARY PUCCOON
(*Lithospermum canescens* (Michx.) Lehm.)

Season and Stature: The Hoary Puccoon is a native cool-season perennial belonging to the Boraginaceae, or borage family. It attains a height of 15 to 45 cm and flowers from April to June.

Flowers: The flowers are orange-yellow. The corolla is tubular and composed of five lobes which are rounded at their tips. The flowers are less than 1 cm long and are borne in dense, short, leafy racemes.

Leaves: The sessile leaves, which are hairy when young, are oblong-linear, tapering to each end.

Use or Importance: The presence of the Hoary Puccoon is an indicator of prairie in good condition. The plant decreases when grazed.

Habitat: Hoary Puccoon is not only a characteristic plant of dry prairies, but it occurs in dry woods, as well.

Range: This species ranges from Ontario to the Dakotas and south to Georgia and Texas.

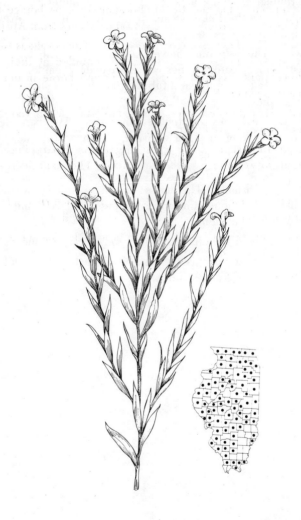

SPIKED LOBELIA
(*Lobelia spicata* Lam.)

Season and Stature: The Spiked Lobelia is a native, warm-season perennial attaining a height up to one meter. Spiked Lobelia belongs to the Lobeliaceae, or lobelia family. It flowers during the Summer aspect.

Flowers: The pale blue flowers are about 0.5 cm long, dense to distant on spicate racemes which are over 30 cm long. The flower is 5-parted, irregular and tubular. There are 2 short petals and 3 larger ones.

Leaves: The leaves are toothed or entire. The basal leaves are broadly oblong, oval, or obovate, narrowed into short petioles, and up to 7 cm long. The upper leaves are sessile, spatulate, and smaller.

Use or Importance: The leaves of many lobelias are acrid and contain poisonous substances. Some drugs and medicines are obtained from them.

Habitat: Spiked Lobelia grows in woods, prairies, and fields.

Range: The range of this species is from eastern Canada to Minnesota, south to Kansas and Arkansas.

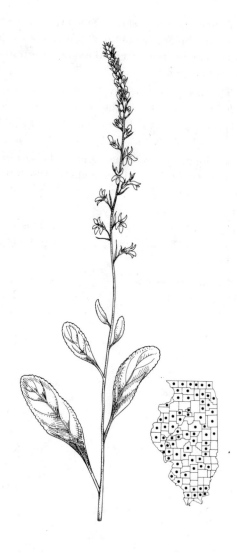

FRINGED LOOSESTRIFE
(*Lysimachia ciliata* L.)

Season and Stature: The Fringed Loosestrife is a native, warm-season perennial belonging to the Primulaceae, or primrose family. It attains a height from 30 cm to nearly 1 meter. It blooms during the Summer aspect.

Flowers: The flowers are pale yellow. There are 5 corolla segments, each up to about 1 cm in length.

Leaves: The leaves are ovate-oblong or ovate-lanceolate, pinnately veined, acuminate at the apex, cordate at the base. The leaves are 5 to 15 cm long. The lower margins of the leaves and the petioles are ciliate, accounting for the common name.

Use or Importance: Pliny believed this plant to take away strife between beasts which were yoked together, and to make them tame.

Habitat: Fringed Loosetrife is found in moist priaries, moist woods, and low ground.

Range: This species ranges all across most of North America north of Mexico.

WILD BERGAMOT
(*Monarda fistulosa* L.)

Season and Stature: Wild Bergamot is a native, warm-season perennial which blooms during the Summer and Fall aspects. It attains a height up to 60 cm or more. It belongs to the Labiatae, or mint family.

Flowers: Many flowers, which are 2-lipped and purplish or lavender, are borne in a spherical head.

Leaves: The ovate-lanceolate leaves are toothed, prominently veined, and arranged oppositely on the square stems.

Use or Importance: The plant, which has flowers that are attractive to bees, is considered a good honey plant. The leaves of several members of the mint family can be used for tea. The plant is not important from the standpoint of grazing and, in fact, is considered as a plant to be ridded from the range. Wild Bergamot can be moved into gardens as an ornamental.

Habitat: This species grows in dry situations of woods and prairies.

Range: Wild Bergamot ranges from New England to Minnesota, south to Texas and Georgia.

COMMON SUNDROPS
(*Oenothera pilosella* Raf.)

Season and Stature: Common Sundrops is a native warm-season perennial belonging to the family Onagraceae. It attains a height of up to 90 cm, and blooms during the Summer aspect.

Flowers: The flowers are bright yellow and open in the morning and the evening. Flowers are 2.5 to 5 cm broad and borne in terminal, leafy-bracted spikes.

Leaves: The leaf shape is lanceolate, ovate, or oval-lanceolate, acute or somewhat obtuse at the tip, narrowed and sessile at the base, and with the lower leaves petioled. The leaves are not coarsely toothed.

Use or Importance: Owing to the brilliance and beauty of this species, it is sometimes brought into gardens.

Habitat: Common Sundrops occurs mostly in dry soil in upland situations. It may be expected in all prairie types except the wettest.

Range: This species is found widely over the True Prairie area and eastward to cover most of the eastern half of the United States.

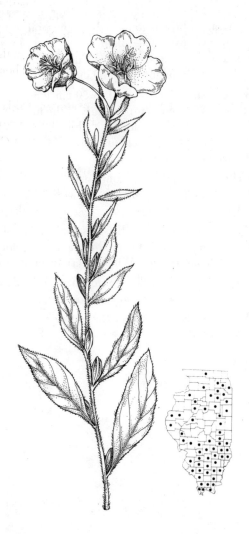

WITCH GRASS
(*Panicum capillare* L.)

Season and Stature: Witch Grass is another native annual species of weedy nature which is found where the prairie has degenerated under abusive use. The plant grows and flowers during the warm-season. It becomes conspicuous during the Fall aspect when it attains a height up to 60 cm.

Flowers: The panicle is from 20 to 30 cm long. It is about half as wide as long. There is a tuft of hairs at the juncture of each of the main panicle branches and the rachis. The spikelets are single-flowered. The entire panicle may break loose and blow about as a "tumbleweed" in autumn.

Leaves: The plant grows in small bunches, or tufts. The leaf blades are 10 to 20 cm long and about 1 cm wide. The leaf sheath is very hairy.

Use or Importance: The Witch Grass serves as an indicator of the condition of prairie. It is never abundant or is seldom present in a vigorous thriving prairie. Witch Grass is not grazed often.

Habitat: Witch Grass may be found on a wide variety of soils. Its presence in prairie would indicate poor or degenerated condition.

Range: Witch Grass occurs over the entire range of both True and Mixed Prairie.

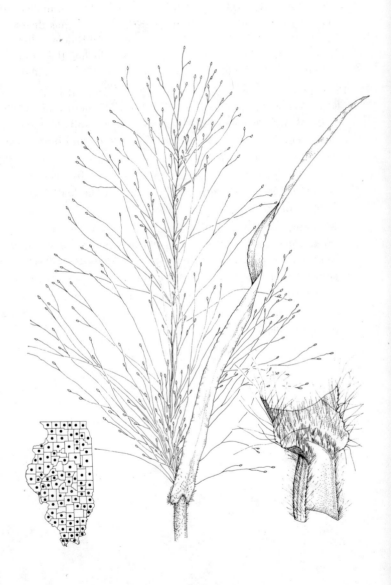

SCRIBNER'S PANIC GRASS
(Panicum oligosanthes Schult. var. *scribnerianum* (Nash) Fern.)

Season and Stature: This species, unlike most species of *Panicum,* is a cool-season grass. It is a native perennial of low stature, being some 20 to 30 cm tall. It grows in tufts. Flowering is in late spring with vegetative growth in early spring. During fall and winter, new, small leaves form a rosette on the ground. Scribner's Panic Grass is a species of minor ranking in the True Prairie area.

Flowers: The panicles are short and bear spikelets which are single-flowered and produce fruits which are 3 to 4 mm long.

Leaves: Leaf blades are short and pointed. Their length is up to 6 cm, and the width up to 2 cm. Fine hairs exist on the undersides of the leaves and upon the leaf base and the sheath.

Use or Importance: The Scribner's Panic Grass provides limited forage for grazing animals. The plant decreases under heavy grazing of prairies.

Habitat: The more open growth of the bunch grasses of upland permits the growth of Scribner's Panic Grass between the other species. It may exist to a lesser extent below taller grasses where it makes a third layer in the structure of True Prairie.

Range: Scribner's Panic Grass grows throughout the United States, except for a few of the southeastern states.

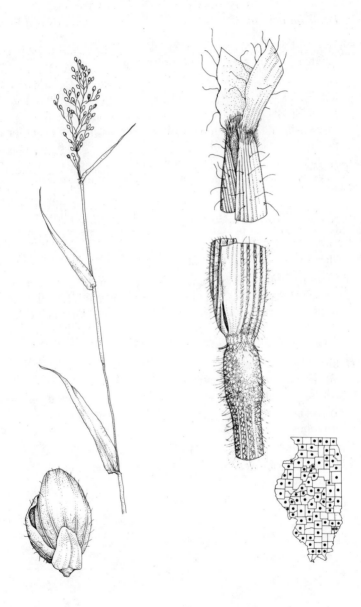

SWITCHGRASS
(*Panicum virgatum* L.)

Season and Stature: Switchgrass is also called Tall Panic Grass. It is a native, warm-season, sod-forming perennial grass. It begins growth in late April or mid-May. The height of Switchgrass is up to 2 meters, but usually somewhat less than that attained by Big Bluestem or Indian Grass.

Flowers: The well developed panicle is often up to 60 cm in length, and bears a good crop of fruits which are from 3 to 6 mm long and up to 1.5 mm wide. The fruits are developed from a single-flowered spikelet. Both glumes are present and well developed.

Leaves: The leaves of Switchgrass are persistent on the plant into winter, and are closely grown to give the lower half of the plant a dense growth appearance. The leaves have a copious patch of hairs or dense pubescence in the form of an inverted "V" shape where the leaf joins the culm.

Use or Importance: Switchgrass is palatable in its early growth and is readily eaten by all kinds of grazing animals. It will decrease under uncontrolled or heavy grazing and should not be grazed too low to the ground. The Switchgrass is popular for reclamation work and in prairie restoration. It is easily established.

Habitat: Switchgrass is a lowland dominant. It grows well in moist bottomland situations. Often its position in the moisture gradient will be just above the wettest habitat, one occupied by Slough Grass and Prairie Cordgrass. It may, however, be found in drier situations such as just above the Big Bluestem and Indian Grass.

Range: Switchgrass may be found over all the True Prairie and Mixed Prairie areas of central United States and the southern Prairies of Texas.

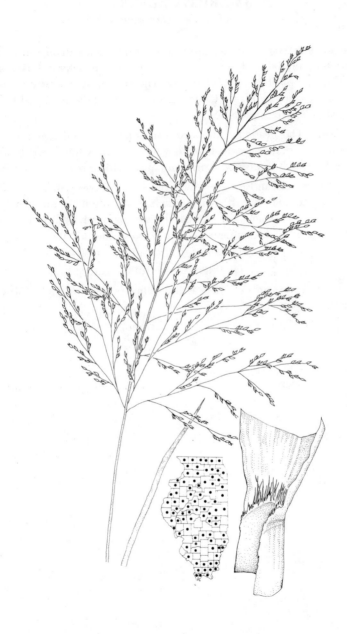

AMERICAN FEVERFEW
(*Parthenium integrifolium* L.)

Season and Stature: The American Feverfew is a native, warm-season perennial having tuberous thickened rootstocks. It belongs to the Compositae, or aster family. The plant attains a height up to one meter. It begins to flower during the Summer aspect and extends into September.

Flowers: The heads are numerous in dense terminal clusters. The disk flowers are perfect but not fertile. The whitish ray flowers are about 5 in number, pistillate and fertile.

Leaves: American Feverfew has firm, rough leaves which are ovate or ovate-oblong with margins which are crenate-dentate. The lower stem leaves and the basal leaves are petioled. The leaves are up to 30 cm long and up to 10 cm or more wide.

Use or Importance: A tea from the leaves has apparently been used in treating fever. The plant is also called wild quinine.

Habitat: American Feverfew is found in dry prairies, rights-of-way of roads, and railroads.

Range: American Feverfew is found from New York to Minnesota, south to Texas and Georgia.

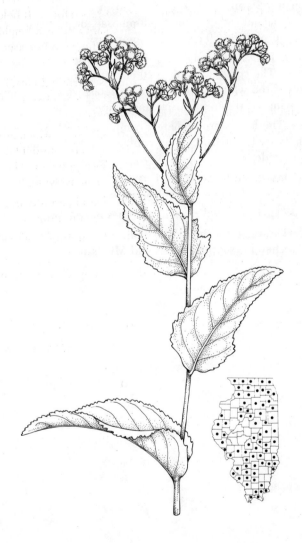

WHITE PRAIRIE CLOVER
(*Petalostemum candidum* (Willd.) Michx.)

Season and Stature: White Prairie Clover is a native, warm-season perennial belonging to the Leguminosae, or pea family. It attains a height of 30 to 60 cm and blooms during the Summer aspect.

Flowers: There are many small flowers densely arranged in short spikes. The spikes are 2.5 to 10 cm long and up to 6 mm thick. Each of the white flowers has four petals which are similar and one which is different in size and shape.

Leaves: The leaves are pinnately compound with 5-7 leaflets. The leaflets are linear-lanceolate to oblong, up to 3 cm long and up to 4 mm wide.

Use or Importance: The White Priarie Clover is palatable to grazing animals and decreases when the prairie is grazed.

Habitat: This species thrives in all types of prairies.

Range: The range of the White Prairie Clover is from Indiana to Saskatchewan, south to Texas and Mississippi.

PURPLE PRAIRIE CLOVER
(*Petalostemum purpureum* (Vent.) Rydb.)

Season and Stature: This handsome herb is a member of the Leguminose, or legume family. It is a native, warm-season herb which grows to a height of 30 to 90 cm. Several stems may grow from a single base.

Flowers: The flowers are pinkish-purple on elongated spikes which are 2 to 4 cm long.

Leaves: The leaves are divided into 3-5 narrow leaflets which may be sparingly hairy.

Use or Importance: This plant is highly palatable and nutritious. It is grazed often and tends to decrease under heavy use. Purple Prairie Clover fixes nitrogen in the soil. It has been reported that tea made from the leaves of this plant has a binding or constipating effect. This plant usually ranks high in abundance among native legumes in the prairie.

Habitat: Purple Prairie Clover is most abundant in the upland of the True Prairie. It also occurs in sand prairies, hill prairies, and gravel-hill prairies.

Range: This species ranges from Saskatchewan and Montana in the north to Tennessee and New Mexico in the south.

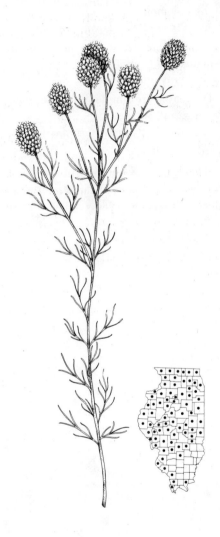

PRAIRIE PHLOX
(*Phlox pilosa* L.)

Season and Stature: The Prairie Phlox is a cool-season herb belonging to the Polemoniaceae, or phlox family. It attains a height of up to 60 cm. Prairie Phlox flowers during the Spring aspect.

Flowers: The inflorescence is cymose-corymbose. The flowers are short-pedicelled, and the five petals are fused into a tubular flower which is pink or purple.

Leaves: The leaves are simple, opposite, linear or lanceolate, 2.5 to 10 cm long, and sessile.

Use or Importance: The Prairie Phlox has been grown successfully as a garden plant.

Habitat: This species is found in prairies and dry woods.

Range: Prairie Phlox ranges from New England to Florida, west to Michigan, Kansas, and Texas.

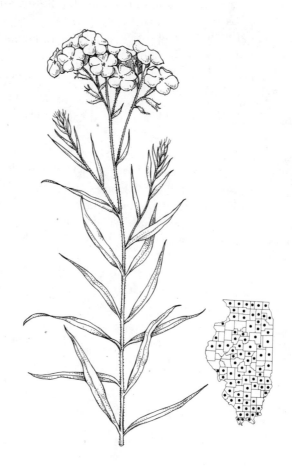

KENTUCKY BLUEGRASS
(*Poa pratensis* L.)

Season and Stature: Kentucky Bluegrass, though a non-native grass, has been included because it is widely represented in prairies today. It has become thoroughly naturalized. Kentucky Bluegrass is adapted to growing in the shade of the taller grasses where it often makes up nearly ten per cent of the composition. Bluegrass is a cool-season, sod-forming grass up to 60 cm in height.

Flowers: The medium-wide panicle supports spikelets which have 2-5 flowers. The bluegrasses have a mass of cobwebby hairs at the base of the lemmas. The flowers and fruits mature in late Spring and early Summer aspect.

Leaves: The leaf blades are long, and uniformly slender to the tip where they terminate in a boat-shaped end.

Use or Importance: Kentucky Bluegrass affords good early grazing. The species is palatable and nutritious and is classed as a soft grass. Under grazing, a prairie will degenerate into a stage of near replacement of other grasses by Kentucky Bluegrass. Thus, bluegrass is an increaser.

Habitat: Kentucky Bluegrass is tolerant of shade and will be found as an understory species to the tall grasses. It may be found in moist to dry conditions.

Range: Kentucky Bluegrass ranges widely in the United States except in areas which are hot and dry. It is found in all Illinois Prairies.

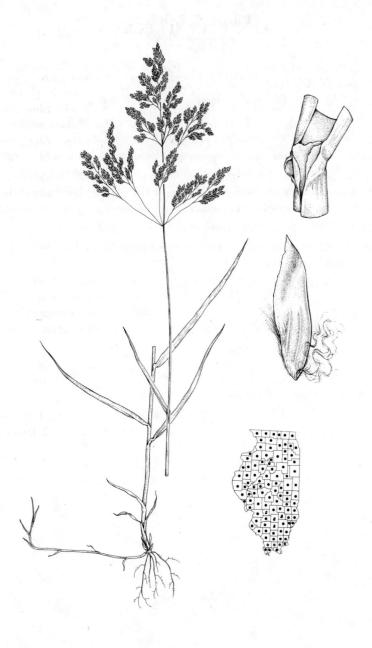

PRAIRIE PARSLEY
(*Polytaenia nuttallii* DC.)

Season and Stature: The Prairie Parsley is a native, cool-season perennial in the Umbelliferae, or parsley family. It attains a height up to 60 cm and flowers during the Spring aspect.

Flowers: The yellow flowers are borne in 6- to 12-rayed umbels. The flower stalks are finely pubescent.

Leaves: The leaves are twice pinnately compound. Each leaf segment is deeply pinnatifid with dentate or entire lobes.

Use or Importance: Many members of the parsley family may be used as condiments and seasonings.

Habitat: Prairie Parsley grows in dry prairies and open woods.

Range: This species ranges from Indiana to Alabama, west to North Dakota and Texas.

SAMPSON'S SNAKEROOT
(*Psoralea psoralioides* (Walt.) Cory)

Season and Stature: The Sampson's Snakeroot is a cool-season perennial belonging to the Leguminosae, or pea family. It attains a height of 30 to 60 cm and blooms during the late Spring aspect. The Illinois plants actually belong to var. *eglandulosa* (Ell.) F. L. Freeman.

Flowers: The flowers are lavender and borne in a dense, spike-like raceme 2.5 to 10 cm long. The flower stalks are much longer than the leaves.

Leaves: The 3 leaflets of each leaf are up to 6 cm long and up to 1.5 cm broad. The middle leaflet is on a longer stalk than the others.

Use or Importance: This species is grazed and tends to disappear under heavy grazing.

Habitat: Sampson's Snakeroot occurs in rocky glades and dry prairies.

Range: This species grows from Virginia and Georgia west to Kansas and Texas.

SCURF PEA
(*Psoralea tenuiflora* Pursh)

Season and Stature: The Scurf Pea is a member of the Leguminosae, or pea family. It is a native, warm-season perennial attaining
a height up to one meter. It flowers in the early Summer aspect.

Flowers: The purplish flowers are about 3 mm long and are borne in
racemes which are up to 6 cm long.

Leaves: The leaves are palmately compound into 3-5 leaflets. The
leaflets are oval or elliptic and up to 1 cm long.

Use or Importance: The Scurf Pea is a palatable and nutritious plant
to grazing animals. It decreases when the prairie is grazed.

Habitat: Scurf Pea occurs in both dry prairies and in open woods.

Range: The range of this species is from Indiana to Nebraska, south
to Arizona and Texas.

MOUNTAIN MINT
(*Pycnanthemum tenuifolium* Schrad.)

Season and Stature: This Mountain Mint is a native, warm-season perennial herb which attains a height up to 60 cm. It blooms from July to September. It belongs to the Labiatae, or mint family.

Flowers: The flowers are tubular, 2-lipped, white dotted with purple, borne in terminal clusters. The upper lip of the flower is entire, while the lower is 3-cleft. The stamens are 4 and about equal in length.

Leaves: The linear to lanceolate leaves are entire and smooth, with the upper sessile and the lower short-petioled. The leaves are opposite on the square stems and have a mint odor.

Use or Importance: A tea is reportedly made from the leaves of this species.

Habitat: This species grows in a variety of dry and moist habitats, including prairies.

Range: This Mountain Mint ranges from New England to Minnesota, south to Texas and Georgia.

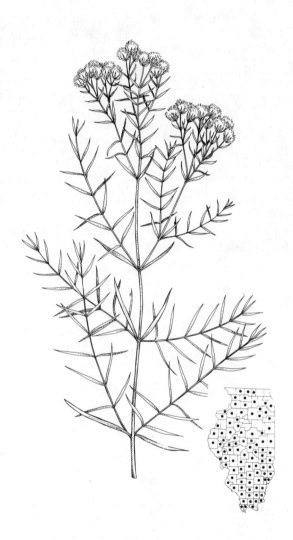

PRAIRIE HYSSOP
(*Pycnanthemum virginiana* (L.) Durand & Jackson)

Season and Stature: The Prairie Hyssop is a native warm-season perennial of the Labiatae, or mint family. It attains a height of 30 to 90 cm and blooms from July to September.

Flowers: The flowers are densely arranged in head-like clusters or glomerules which are about 0.5 cm in diameter. Each flower is small, pubescent, and purple-spotted. The corolla tube is longer than the calyx.

Leaves: The leaves are lanceolate, acute at the tip, entire, fragrant, and sessile. Some of the leaves are minutely hairy.

Use or Importance: The leaves can be used as seasoning in cooking.

Habitat: Prairie Hyssop occurs in dry pastures and gravel hill prairies.

Range: This species is found from Maine to North Carolina, west to North Dakota and Kansas.

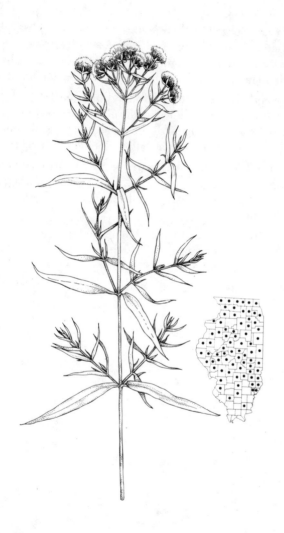

DROOPING CONEFLOWER
(*Ratibida pinnata* (Vent.) Barnh.)

Season and Stature: The Drooping Coneflower, sometimes called Weary Susan or the Gray-headed Coneflower, is a member of the Compositae family. It is a native, warm-season, tall perennial which attains a height of about 1 m. It flowers from June to September.

Flowers: The flowers are grouped in a head. The rays, which are yellow and turned downward, number from 4 to 10. The rays are 2.5 to 7 cm long and up to nearly 1 cm wide. The disk is gray-green and twice as tall as thick.

Leaves: The lower leaves are pinnately 3 to 7 parted, with the segments lanceolate, dentate, cleft, or entire. They are petiolate. The upper leaves are sessile or nearly so. All leaves are very smooth.

Use or Importance: The Drooping Coneflower decreases when the prairie is overgrazed. It is attractive to grazing animals in its young growth.

Habitat: Drooping Coneflower is found in many prairie situations.

Range: This species ranges from Ontario to Minnesota, south to Georgia and Nebraska.

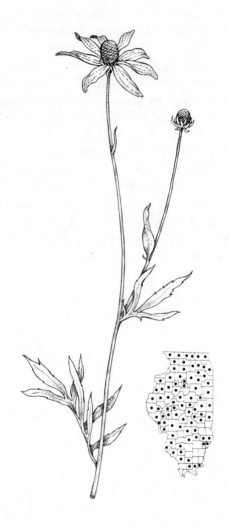

CAROLINA ROSE
(*Rosa carolina* L.)

Season and Stature: The Carolina Rose is a native, warm-season perennial herb attaining a height of up to 90 cm. It is a member of the Rosaceae, or rose family. It flowers during the Summer aspect.

Flowers: The pale pink flowers are usually solitary on the branches. Each flower is 3 to 5 cm broad. The fruit is about 0.5 cm high.

Leaves: The leaves are pinnately compound, composed of 5 to 9 leaflets. The leaflets are usually elliptic and up to 4 cm long. They are conspicuously toothed. The stems which bear the leaves are sparsely prickly.

Use or Importance: The fruits, called rose hips, are rich in Vitamin C. These hips may be used to make jelly.

Habitat: The Carolina Rose grows in dry, sandy, rocky, or clay soils in thin woods, open fields, and prairies.

Range: This species occurs throughout the eastern United States, extending westward to Minnesota and Texas.

BROWN-EYED SUSAN
(*Rudbeckia hirta* L.)

Season and Stature: The handsome, familiar Brown-eyed Susan is a native, warm-season perennial herb belonging to the Compositae, or aster family. Brown-eyed Susan grows to a height up to 70 cm. It flowers throughout the later Summer aspect and the Fall aspect.

Flowers: The showy yellow rays, 10 to 20 in number, are about 1.5 to 2 cm long. The brown disk is about 1.5 to 2 cm broad and dome-shaped. Each head is about 6-7 cm broad.

Leaves: The lower leaves are oblong, toothed, and somewhat hairy or rough. The upper leaves are oblong-lanceolate, smaller, sessile, and alternate in their arrangement on the hairy stems.

Use or Importance: This plant is often brought into gardens because of its showy flowers. The plant is not a palatable species for grazing.

Habitat: This species is found in all Illinois prairies. In some Illinois hill prairies, a shorter, later-blooming species is *Rudbeckia missouriensis*.

Range: The Brown-eyed Susan is widely distributed across the prairies and plains from Canada to Texas and west to the Rockies.

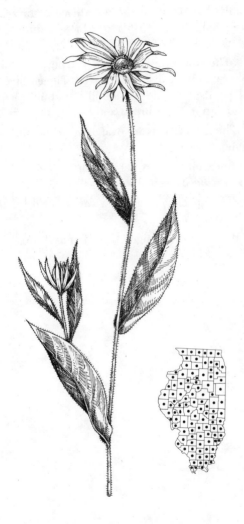

WILD PETUNIA
(*Ruellia humilis* Nutt.)

Season and Stature: The Wild Petunia is a native, warm-season perennial belonging to the Acanthaceae, or acanthus family. It attains a height up to 70 cm and blooms during the Summer and Fall aspects.

Flowers: The flowers are purple to pale purple or blue and clustered or solitary in the axils of the leaves. The corolla is composed of 5 fused petals to make a tube-like, petunia-shaped flower. The flower is up to 3 cm broad and from 3 to 5 cm long.

Leaves: The hairy leaves are oval or ovate, sessile, and from 3.5 to 7 cm long.

Use or Importance: It has been reported that some members of the genus *Ruellia* have been used as sources of dyes and of drugs.

Habitat: This species occurs in a variety of dry habitats, including prairies and woods.

Range: Wild Petunia ranges from Pennsylvania to Iowa, south to Texas and Florida.

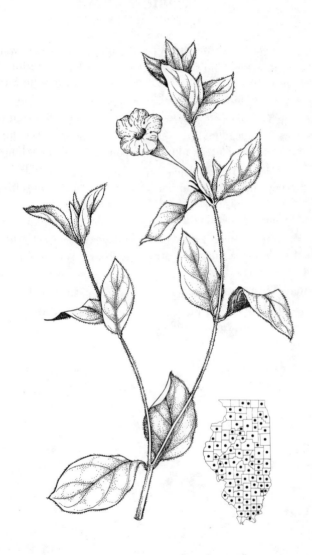

PRAIRIE WILLOW
(*Salix humilis* Marsh.)

Season and Stature: Prairie Willow is a low shrub belonging to the Salicaceae, or willow family. It attains a height up to 2 meters, but less than this under the influence of mowing. Prairie Willow is a cool-season plant which blooms during April and May.

Flowers: The flowering spikes, or catkins, appear much before the leaves. The catkins are sessile, oblong-ovoid, and dense. The female, or pistillate, catkins are about 2.5 to 3.0 cm long in fruit.

Leaves: Prairie Willow leaves are oblanceolate, petioled, up to 15 cm long, and up to one cm wide. They taper to each end. The upper surface is dark green, the lower is densely gray-hairy. The leaves have obliquely lanceolate to ovate stipules.

Use or Importance: Twigs of all willows have a pliability which makes them useful in basketry. The Prairie Willow can be used in this manner.

Habitat: This species occurs in dry soil of prairies.

Range: Prairie Willow ranges from northeastern Canada to Minnesota, south to Kansas and Louisiana.

LITTLE BLUESTEM
(*Schizachyrium scoparium* (Michx.) Nash)

Season and Stature: Little Bluestem is a native, warm-season perennial mid-grass with bunch-forming habit. It grows from May until frost and achieves heights up to more than one meter.

Flowers: Spikelets are formed along numerous racemes which are up to 10 cm long. The spikelets are borne in pairs, some sessile and fertile, one pedicelled and sterile. Up to 200 flower stalks may be in a bunch.

Leaves: In early growth the leaves are 3-8 mm wide, flattened at their base. Where the blades join the sheath is a narrow, whitish transverse line. The leaves are folded.

Use or Importance: Little Bluestem is a palatable and nutritious range grass and decreases under heavy or uncontrolled grazing. When grazed at levels near the ground, it is replaced by weedy species. Success has been achieved in planting this species.

Habitat: Little Bluestem is an upland dominant and ranges from scattered mingling with tall grasses to the extreme upland. In upland it is usually clearly a dominant. It has a much branched fibrous root system which penetrates to depths of 1½ meters. It grows in sandy or rocky soil and is frequent in old fields.

Range: Little Bluestem is found in virtually all the natural grasslands of the United States, except the California and Palouse prairies. Several ecotypes exist.

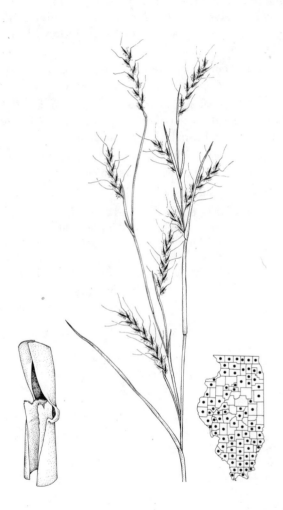

PRAIRIE GROUNDSEL
(*Senecio pauperculus* Michx.)

Season and Stature: Prairie Groundsel is a warm-season perennial which belongs to the Compositae, or aster family. It reaches a height of 50 cm and blooms during the late Spring and early Summer aspects.

Flowers: There are several yellow flower heads at the top of the stem. Each head is up to 2 cm across and has several yellow rays.

Leaves: Several more or less elliptic, long-petiolate leaves are clustered at the base of the plant. The leaves on the stem are alternate and usually deeply jagged.

Use or Importance: Prairie Groundsel adds brightness to the prairie scene during the late Spring aspect.

Habitat: This species is found in prairies and on cliffs.

Range: Prairie Groundsel ranges throughout most of North America except for the southeastern United States.

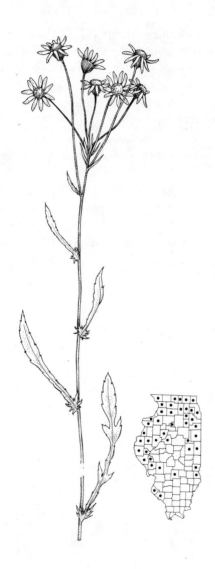

ROSINWEED
(*Silphium integrifolium* Michx.)

Season and Stature: The Rosinweed is a native, warm-season perennial belonging to the Compositae, or aster family. It attains a height up to nearly two meters. It blooms during the Fall aspect.

Flowers: The yellow heads are up to 5 cm broad. They are composed of both disk and ray flowers. The rays are about 0.5 cm long and number up to 25.

Leaves: The opposite leaves are ovate-lanceolate, acuminate, entire or toothed, and rough to the touch. They are sessile and measure from 7 to 15 cm long and 2.5 to 5 cm wide.

Use or Importance: The Rosinweed is palatable and nutritious when young and is readily grazed. It decreases when the prairie is grazed.

Habitat: This species is common in the prairies of Illinois.

Range: Rosinweed ranges from Wisconsin south to Alabama and Kansas.

COMPASS PLANT
(*Silphium laciniatum* L.)

Season and Stature: The Compass Plant is a warm-season perennial herb in the Compositae, or aster family. It attains a height up to 3.5 meters and flowers during the Fall aspect.

Flowers: The yellow heads are borne at the tips of the branches. Each head has both ray and disk flowers. The green bracts on the back of each head are in more than 2 series.

Leaves: The leaves are large, deeply cleft, and rough to the touch. They are usually placed edgewise to the north-south direction, hence the common name.

Use or Importance: Compass Plant was important in the diet of bison, and it is eaten by cattle. Thus, the plant behaves as a decreaser under grazing.

Habitat: This species is a common inhabitant of prairies.

Range: This midwestern species ranges from Michigan to South Dakota, south to Texas and Mississippi.

CUP-PLANT
(*Silphium perfoliatum* L.)

Season and Stature: The Cup-plant is a native, warm-season perennial belonging to the Compositae, or aster family. It attains a
height of 1 to 2 meters. Cup-plant flowers during the Fall aspect.

Flowers: The heads are numerous and composed of both disk and
ray flowers. These heads are 2.5 to 7.5 cm broad and yellow, with
20 to 30 rays. Each ray is about 2.5 cm long.

Leaves: The leaves are a distinguishing part of the plant, being
broadly triangular to ovate. The upper leaves are connate-per-
foliate or clasping on the squarrish, stout stems in a manner to
form a cup-like area. The lower leaves have blades which contract
into winged petioles. The larger leaves are up to 35 cm long and
up to 20 cm wide.

Use or Importance: Cup-plant is palatable and nutritious and decreases in prairies when they are grazed.

Habitat: Cup-plant grows in prairies, woods, and other rather open
areas.

Range: This species grows from central Ontario across to South
Dakota, south to Oklahoma and Georgia.

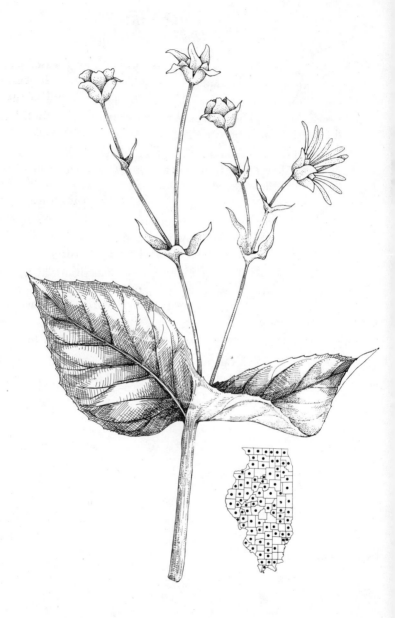

PRAIRIE DOCK
(*Silphium terebinthinaceum* Jacq.)

Season and Stature: The Prairie Dock is a native, warm-season perennial herb belonging to the Compositae, or aster family. It is one of the four Illinois species of *Silphium*. The flowering stem usually attains a height in excess of 2 meters. Prairie Dock blooms during the Fall aspect.

Flowers: The numerous, yellow heads have both ray and disk flowers. They range from 3.5 to 8 cm broad. The rays number from 12 to 20 per head.

Leaves: The leaves are a most distinctive part of this plant in that they are rough like sandpaper and are confined to the base of the plant. The leaves are broadly ovate and cordate at the base. The blades are often more than 40 cm long and up to 30 cm wide.

Use or Importance: This species forms a gum or rosin which is used in various ways. It was chewed by early settlers as a gum. The plant is palatable in young growth and tends to decrease when prairie is grazed.

Habitat: This species is a characteristic plant of prairies.

Range: Prairie Dock ranges throughout most of the Midwest, but does not occur west of Iowa.

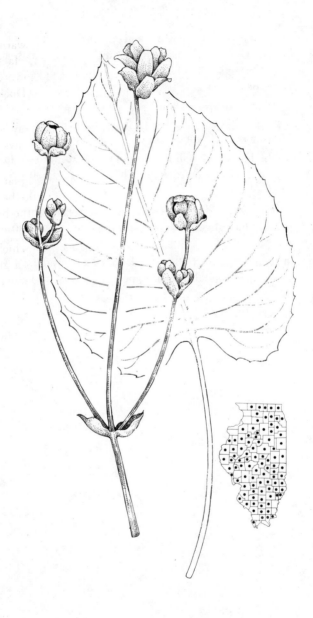

NARROW-LEAVED BLUE-EYED GRASS
(*Sisyrinchium angustifolium* Mill.)

Season and Stature: The Narrow-leaved Blue-eyed Grass is a native, perennial, cool-season herb belonging to the Iridaceae, or iris family. It attains a height of 10 to 60 cm and blooms during the Spring aspect.

Flowers: The color of the flowers is deep violet-blue. There are six perianth parts, each less than 1 cm long. The ovary is inferior. The flower is subtended by a green spathe.

Leaves: The leaves are half the height of the stem to slightly longer and up to 2 mm or more wide. They are produced from winged stems.

Use or Importance: The plants have underground rootstocks which apparently have been eaten by pigs, as the plants also have the name "pigroot."

Habitat: Narrow-leaved Blue-eyed Grass is found in a variety of habitats, including all prairie types.

Range: This species is found across the eastern half of Canada, south to Kansas, Illinois, and Ohio.

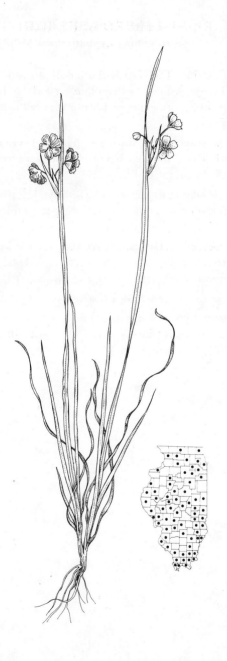

TALL GOLDENROD
(*Solidago canadensis* L.)

Season and Stature: The Tall Goldenrod is a warm-season perennial belonging to the Compositae, or aster family. It attains a height up to 2 meters, and blooms during the Fall aspect.

Flowers: The yellow heads are borne in abundance on spreading or recurving branches of the large panicle. The individual flower heads are 2 to 3 mm high. The disk flowers are mostly perfect. The ray flowers are pistillate.

Leaves: The leaves are lanceolate, 3-nerved, tapered to each end, and rough above. The lower leaves are smaller and sessile, or nearly so.

Use or Importance: This goldenrod may be used to make a mildly stimulating tea.

Habitat: Tall Goldenrod grows in a variety of open habitats, including prairies, fields, and roadsides.

Range: The range of this species is from Quebec to Minnesota, south to Texas and Florida.

GRASS-LEAVED GOLDENROD
(*Solidago graminifolia* (L.) Salisb.)

Season and Stature: The Grass-leaved Goldenrod is a native, warm-season perennial belonging to the Compositae, or aster family. It attains a height up to 120 cm and blooms during the Summer aspect.

Flowers: The yellow ray flowers are pistillate and more numerous than the disk flowers, which are perfect. The rays number from 12 to 20, the disk flowers from 8 to 12. The heads are in somewhat flat-topped inflorescences.

Leaves: The leaves are linear-lanceolate, numerous, narrowed at each end, up to 15 cm long and up to 0.5 cm wide. They have 3 to 5 veins.

Use or Importance: Virtually all species of Goldenrod take easily to cultivation. Almost all species possess aromatic, mildly stimulating properties used for teas. Their splendor in the autumn landscape is pleasing.

Habitat: Grass-leaved Goldenrod grows in prairies and fields.

Range: This species occurs from Minnesota, south to Ohio and Missouri.

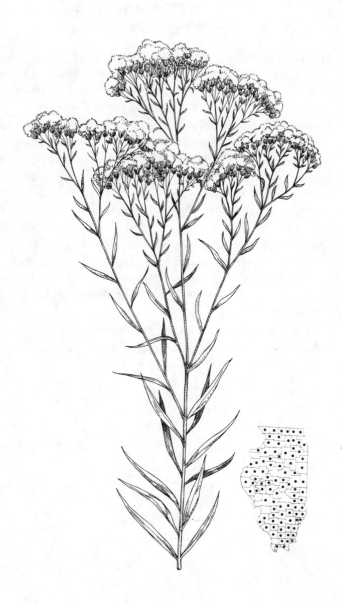

STIFF GOLDENROD
(*Solidago rigida* L.)

Season and Stature: The Stiff Goldenrod is a native perennial recognized by its broad, flat-topped inflorescence. The plant is a member of the Compositae, or aster family. It attains a height of over one meter. It flowers during the Fall aspect.

Flowers: The goldenrod flowers are like miniature asters and are all yellow. They are arranged in an inflorescence which is about 15 cm across and flat across the top.

Leaves: Stiff, rough textured leaves are alternately arranged on the stem. The leaves on the lower part of the plant are oblong and have short petioles. The upper leaves are lanceolate and are sessile. There are also longer basal leaves which overwinter.

Use or Importance: Stiff Goldenrod is more palatable than other members of the goldenrod group but is still infrequently grazed. It behaves in prairie as an invader, *i.e.*, it tends to come into pastures in greater amount when the prairie has been weakened by grazing.

Habitat: This species grows in prairies and dry woods.

Range: The range of the Stiff Goldenrod is from Massachusetts to Saskatchewan, south to Texas and Georgia.

INDIAN GRASS
(*Sorghastrum nutans* (L.) Nash)

Season and Stature: This native, warm-season perennial grass is a codominant with Big Bluestem. It also attains heights between 1.5 to 2.0 or even 2.5 meters. Growth begins at about the same time as Big Bluestem, which is about the first of May. Flowering is during late July and August.

Flowers: The flowers are yellowish, a color imparted by the conspicuous extrusion of the yellow anthers. The spikelets are borne in pairs, one sessile and perfect, the other reduced to a hairy pedicel. The spikelets are borne on short racemes which branch from the rachis in paniculate fashion. The fertile spikelets terminate in a bent awn which is about four times the length of the fruit itself.

Leaves: In its young growth, Indian Grass somewhat resembles Big Bluestem. Its leaves depart the stem (culm) at about a 45 degree angle. The blade, about 1.5 cm wide, noticeably narrows or tapers where it joins the culm. At the juncture of leaf and culm is a notched ligule about 2 to 3 mm in length.

Use or Importance: Indian Grass is a palatable grass for grazing or as a component of prairie hay. It is nutritious and is sought out by grazing animals. It will decrease under heavy grazing. It probably should not be allowed to be grazed to heights under five inches or it will be replaced in the sward by less palatable species. The seeds can be harvested by combine and are often used in reclamation projects or in restoration of prairie.

Habitat: Indian Grass may frequently invade the drier uplands and particularly where there has been some mild disturbance such as an occasional burning.

Range: Indian Grass grows throughout the United States where tall grass can be supported. It is especially adapted to True Prairie and the Texas prairies. In Mixed Prairie, it will be found mostly in ravines and valley bottoms.

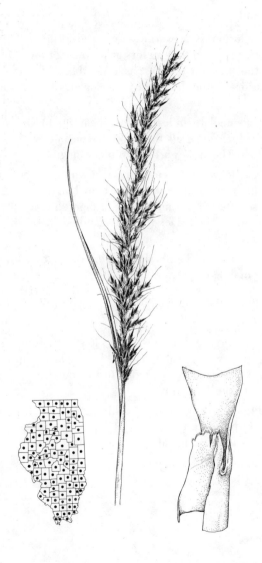

PRAIRIE CORDGRASS
(*Spartina pectinata* Link)

Season and Stature: Growing in the wettest part of the prairie is the Prairie Cordgrass, a warm-season, sod-forming perennial which attains heights up to 2 meters at flowering time. Most ecologists place the Prairie Cordgrass as a member of the last stage in the succession of the hydrosere. It flowers during the early Fall aspect.

Flowers: Paniculate inflorescences bear up to six or more short spikes which have all the spikelets on one side of the panicle branches. The spikes are up to 6 cm long.

Leaves: The leaves are 1 cm or more in width and have a prominent midvein. Leaves are up to 80 cm in length, light green color, finely serrated at the margins, and tapered gradually throughout their length. The leaves must be handled with care or fingers or hands may be cut.

Use or Importance: The Prairie Cordgrass is grazed if early season use is possible or permitted. In late season, this species becomes unpalatable and serves only as thatching material. Cordgrass is a good grass for the protection of waterways and for erosion control.

Habitat: The Prairie Cordgrass favors low, wet, poorly aerated soils. It may grow where water stands a few inches deep in the Spring. These wet meadows often dry to the point where they can be mowed in the Summer.

Range: Prairie Cordgrass grows throughout the United States except for the extreme southwest and extreme southeast. It was abundant in the original wet prairie of Illinois.

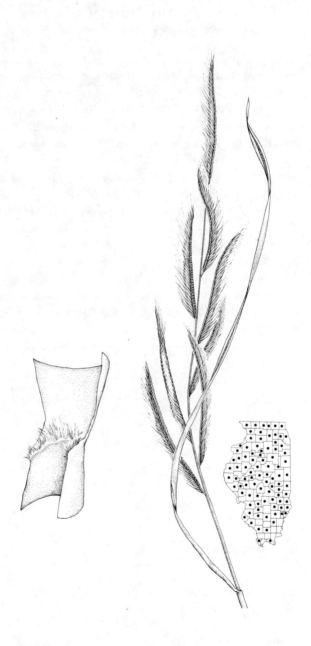

TALL DROPSEED
(*Sporobolus asper* (Michx.) Kunth)

Season and Stature: The Tall Dropseed is a native, warm-season perennial which has short rhizomes and tends to grow locally in pure stands. It attains a height up to one meter. It flowers and produces its fruits in late Summer or early Fall aspects.

Flowers: A narrow panicle is enclosed by an inflated sheath. Only one-third to one-half of the inflorescence emerges, and the fruits fall freely from the glumes, hence the name "dropseed."

Leaves: The leaves of Tall Dropseed are long and narrow and tapering. They tend to have about ¼ of their length appearing dead or dry at the tips when mature. The leaf sheaths are hairy at the throat and the leaves are somewhat hairy at their base. The leaves bleach to a light color in winter.

Use or Importance: The main use of most grasses is grazing. Tall Dropseed is known as a hard grass because of its high proportion of fibers. It is not as palatable as the bluestems and behaves as an increaser for a time since it does not receive first choice by the grazing animal.

Habitat: Tall Dropseed grows on slopes and level upland areas where the ground is packed or hard. Because it grows in pure stands it is suspected of allelopathic properties.

Range: Tall Dropseed is most common and widespread in Mixed Prairie, where it is well adapted to the drier conditions. It is successful in True Prairie in dry open areas.

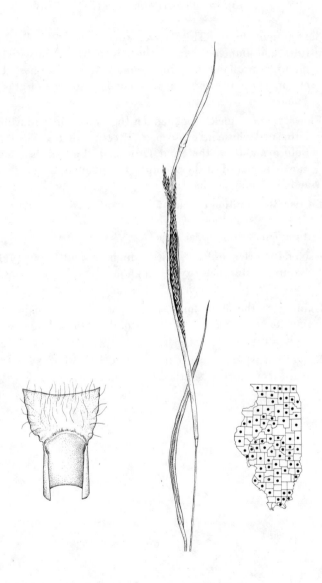

SAND DROPSEED
(*Sporobolus cryptandrus* (Torr.) Gray)

Season and Stature: This native, warm-season perennial grows in tufts and bunches because it has short rhizomes. The plant matures and flowers in late Summer. It attains a height up to 60 cm or more. It is a minor or secondary species of grass in True Prairie.

Flowers: The panicle is open and is therefore different from the Tall Dropseed whose inflorescence scarcely emerges from the sheath. Before maturity, the Sand Dropseed also has its inflorescence mostly enclosed in the sheath. The spikelets are single-flowered and fall freely at maturity.

Leaves: Recognition of Sand Dropseed is easy in vegetative condition because of the presence of copious white hairs radiating in all directions at the nodal areas.

Use or Importance: Palatability is high in Sand Dropseed before it matures. After maturity it is high in fibers and becomes a "hard" grass. The plant is considered as an invader in True Prairie.

Habitat: As the name implies, the plant is well adapted to sandy soils. Sand Dropseed is tolerant of drought and increases during such periods.

Range: This species occurs throughout the United States and Canada, except for the southeastern United States.

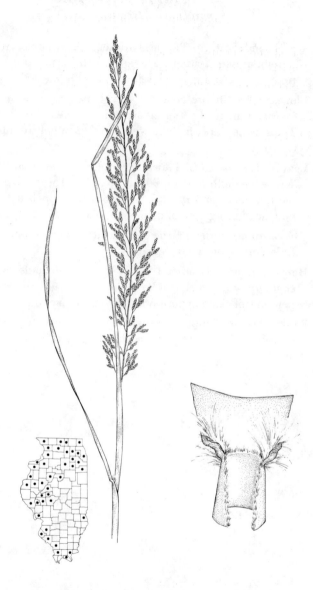

PRAIRIE DROPSEED
(*Sporobolus heterolepis* (Gray) Gray)

Season and Stature: Prairie Dropseed is a native, warm-season perennial which attains a height up to one meter at flowering time. It is a mid-grass and flowers during the Fall aspect.

Flowers: The inflorescence is a well developed panicle. Before flowering maturity, the inflorescence is held within the sheath. The spikelets are single-flowered and soon fall from the inflorescence.

Leaves: The leaves of Prairie Dropseed are long and attenuated. The leaf length is often 60 cm or more. The final ⅓ of the leaf tends to become dry. The plant has the bunch habit, with the bunches having a basal diameter of about 15 to 20 cm.

Use or Importance: Prairie Dropseed is a palatable species and decreases under heavy grazing.

Habitat: Prairie Dropseed grows on the uplands and forms a community in which it is a dominant. It makes up from 50 to 80 per cent of the composition. It grows in dry soil.

Range: Prairie Dropseed ranges from Quebec to Saskatchewan, south to Texas, Arkansas, and New York.

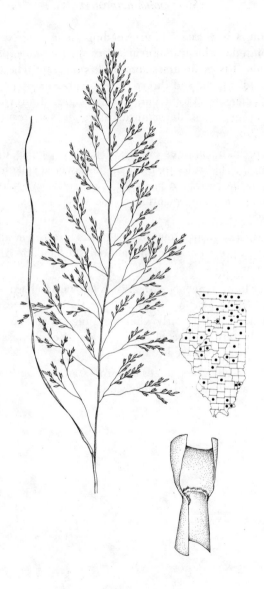

NEEDLEGRASS
(*Stipa spartea* Trin.)

Season and Stature: The Needlegrass is named for its sharp-pointed, callus-tipped fruit. It is sharp as a needle, and its long awns (10 cm or more) resemble a thread. The grass has been called "needle and thread." Needlegrass is a cool-season grass of mid-height (30 to 90 cm). It begins growth in April, and flowers by June. It is dormant in Summer and resumes growth in September.

Flowers: The inflorescence is a narrow panicle up to 25 cm in length. The fruits are from single-flowered spikelets and they fall from the glumes at maturity. The fruits have a hygroscopic awn which aids the "planting of the fruit" by its own self-induced mechanism.

Leaves: The plant grows in small tufts 6 to 10 cm in diameter. The leaves are ribbed on the abaxial side and the other surface is smooth. The leaves are long-tapering.

Use or Importance: Needlegrass is known as a hard grass because of its high proportion of fiber. Despite this feature, Needlegrass is palatable, particularly when in young growth, and due to its early availability as a cool-season grass. Needlegrass behaves as a decreaser in grazed prairies.

Range: Needlegrass ranges all across Canada, south to New Mexico, Kansas, Ohio, and Pennsylvania.

GOAT'S-RUE
(*Tephrosia virginiana* (L.) Pers.)

Season and Stature: The Goat's-rue is a native, warm-season member of the Leguminosae, or pea family. It grows from several stems and reaches a height of 30 to 60 cm. It flowers during the Summer aspect.

Flowers: The large flowers are up to 2 cm long and borne in terminal racemes. The flowers are multi-colored in tints of cream, pink, and purple. The petals assume the typical shape found in the pea family.

Leaves: The leaves are pinnately compound, with the 15-31 leaflets tapering at each end and silky-hairy.

Use or Importance: Goat's-rue is a nutritious, palatable plant which is relished by livestock of all kinds. It decreases in prairies where grazing is permitted and where the stocking rate is heavy. The plant is considered a sensitive indicator of the condition of prairie rangeland.

Habitat: This handsome herb is found in hill prairies and sand prairies and on a wide variety of upland sites.

Range. Goat's-rue grows throughout most of the eastern United States, from New Hampshire and Florida in the east to South Dakota and Texas in the west.

AMERICAN GERMANDER
(*Teucrium canadense* L.)

Season and Stature: The American Germander, also known as Wood Sage, is a member of the Labiatae, or mint family. It is a native, warm-season perennial attaining a height up to 60 cm. It flowers from June to the end of Summer.

Flowers: The spikes are dense and up to 25 cm long. The two-lipped flowers are about 1 cm long, on very short pedicels. The flowers are tubular and pinkish in color.

Leaves: The arrangement of leaves on the square stems is opposite. The leaves are prominently pinnately veined, oblong-lanceolate to ovate-lanceolate, pointed at the tip, and rounded at the base. The margins are toothed, and the leaves are hairy beneath.

Use or Importance: This species has little importance as a forage plant.

Habitat: American Germander grows in moist prairies and at the edge of thickets.

Range: The range of this species is from northeastern Canada to Minnesota, south to Texas and Florida.

PRAIRIE SPIDERWORT
(*Tradescantia bracteata* Small)

Season and Stature: The Prairie Spiderwort is a cool-season perennial in the Commelinaceae, or spiderwort family. It attains a height of 35 to 45 cm. It blooms during the Spring aspect.

Flowers: The flowers are borne in terminal cymes subtended by two long, leaf-like bracts which are broader than the leaves. The calyx is 3-parted, green, symmetrical, and glandular-viscid. The 3 petals are rose-colored.

Leaves: The leaves and stems are smooth, 10 to 20 cm long, 0.5 to 1.5 cm wide.

Use or Importance: Most all the spiderworts can be moved into culture in gardens.

Habitat: This species grows in sandy prairies. It is uncommon in Illinois.

Range: Prairie Spiderwort ranges from Michigan and Indiana westward.

SPIDERWORT
(*Tradescantia ohiensis* Raf.)

Season and Stature: The Spiderwort is a cool-season perennial in the Commelinaceae, or spiderwort family. It attains a height of 20 to 60 cm and flowers during the Spring aspect.

Flowers: The three petals of the flowers are deep blue. The green sepals are smooth or with a tuft of non-glandular hairs at the tip.

Leaves: The smooth leaves are long and slender, up to 45 cm long and up to 3.5 cm broad.

Use or Importance: This species is sometimes cultivated because of its beauty.

Habitat: This species occurs in most prairie types, especially the tall grass prairies. It also grows along the margins of woods and along roadsides and gravel or cinder-banked railroad rights-of-way.

Range: The Spiderwort ranges from New England to Florida, west to Minnesota and Texas.

COMMON SPIDERWORT
(*Tradescantia virginiana* L.)

Season and Stature: The Common Spiderwort is a cool-season perennial which may reach a height of 30 cm. It blooms during the Spring aspect. It is a member of the Commelinaceae, or spiderwort family.

Flowers: The flowers, which are usually blue, are borne in terminal cymes subtended by two long, leaf-like bracts. The three sepals are green and without glands. There are also three petals.

Leaves: The leaves are up to 25 cm long and nearly 2 cm broad. They are smooth.

Use or Importance: Because of the beauty of the flowers of this species, it is a favorite in gardens.

Habitat: This species grows in prairies as well as in woodlands.

Range: Common Spiderwort is found from New England to Wisconsin, south to Missouri and Georgia.

EASTERN GAMA GRASS
(*Tripsacum dactyloides* L.)

Season and Stature: Eastern Gama Grass is a species of minor importance in our prairies due to its limited occurrence. It is a native, warm-season perennial which grows in large bunches. The rhizomes are nearly as thick as one's finger. The plant may attain a height up to 9 feet at flowering time. July and August are the months it may be found in flower.

Flowers: The inflorescence is made up of 1 to 3 spikes bearing the staminate flowers above and the pistillate flowers below. These spikes are 15 to 25 cm long. The fruits are embedded or sunken in the rachis of the lower ⅓ or ¼ of the spike. These break into individual units at maturity.

Leaves: The leaves are long and up to 3.5 cm wide, tapering, and extremely sharp along their edges.

Use or Importance: Eastern Gama Grass is palatable when grazed in its early growth. It becomes harsh and unpalatable later. Gama Grass is considered by some as one of the remote ancestors of corn.

Habitat: In the moisture gradient the Eastern Gama Grass grows where it is very moist. It will often be bordered on one side by Slough Grass and Prairie Cordgrass, and on the drier side by Switch Grass. It sometimes accompanies Big Bluestem.

Range: This species ranges from New England to Michigan and Nebraska, south to Texas and Florida.

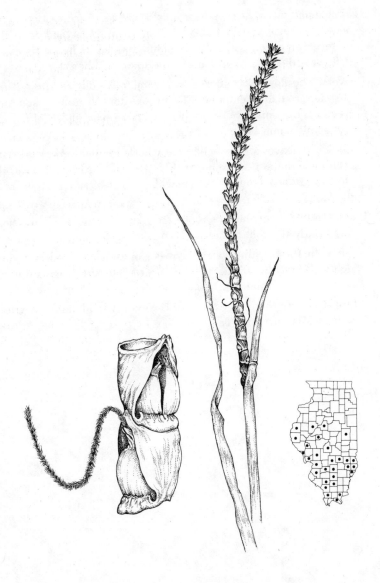

CULVER'S-ROOT
(*Veronicastrum virginicum* (L.) Farw.)

Season and Stature: Culver's-root is a native, warm-season, tall perennial herb, which attains a height of up to one and one-half meters. It is a member of the Scrophulariaceae, or figwort family. It flowers during the period of June to September.

Flowers: The flowers are borne in several spike-like racemes. The racemes are 6 to 20 cm long. Flowers are densely crowded on the racemes; the corollas are tubular, white to pale bluish in color, and about 2 mm long.

Leaves: The leaves are verticillate or whorled in 3-several leaves at each node, opposite in some of the uppermost leaves. The leaf is about 7 to 20 cm long and 2.5 cm wide, serrulate, and narrowed at the base.

Use or Importance: Culver's-root is also known as Culver's physic. Apparently the root has cathartic qualities.

Habitat: In Illinois, this species grows along railroad and highway rights-of-way where relict patches of prairie occur. The habitat is one of good soil and moist condition. It also occurs in dry woods.

Range: Culver's-root ranges from the New England states to Minnesota, Missouri, and Texas.

AMERICAN VETCH
(*Vicia americana* Muhl.)

Season and Stature: The American Vetch is a perennial, warm-season herb belonging to the Leguminosae, or pea family. It is a plant with a trailing habit, attaining a length up to 90 cm. It blooms during the Spring and Summer aspects.

Flowers: The inflorescence is a 3- to 9-flowered raceme. The bluish-purple flowers are about 1 cm long and typically pea-shaped.

Leaves: The leaflets of the compound leaves are 8 to 18 in number, eliptical, sharply toothed, 1 to 2 cm long, and 17 cm wide.

Use or Importance: Palatable forage for livestock is provided by the American Vetch. It is also often seeded along highways or new road shoulders or cuts to help stabilize the soil. It forms a good cover in such situations.

Habitat: American Vetch occurs in prairies which usually show some disturbance.

Range: This species ranges over most of North America north of Mexico, but in Illinois it is found only in the northern one-third of the state.

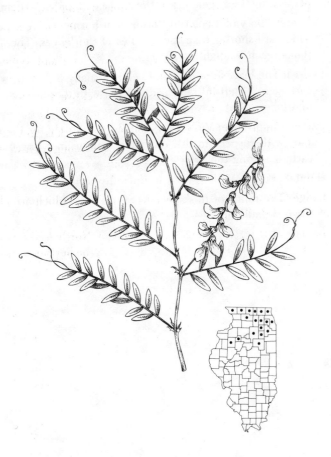

PRAIRIE VIOLET
(*Viola pedatifida* G. Don)

Season and Stature: The Prairie Violet is a very early Spring bloomer, usually flowering before all but the cool-season grasses begin growth. It belongs to the Violaceae, or violet family.

Flowers: The violet-colored flowers are borne on erect peduncles which are shorter than the petioles of the leaves. The flowering stalks reach a height of 10 cm.

Leaves: The leaves are palmately cleft, usually 3-parted, with each part again 3-cleft into linear divisions, with these again cut into 2 to 4 lobes.

Use or Importance: Violets are usually noted only for their beauty and, with respect to this one, it is unique in being one of the earliest among the prairie flowers.

Habitat: Prairie Violet grows in upland prairies.

Range: The range of this species is from Ohio to Alberta, south to Arizona and Illinois.

ARROW-LEAVED VIOLET
(*Viola sagittata* Ait.)

Season and Stature: The Arrow-leaved Violet is a native, cool-season species, which blooms during the Spring aspect. It belongs to the Violaceae, or violet family.

Flowers: The flowers are on peduncles about as long as the leaves. Each flower is violet-purple and up to 2.5 cm long.

Leaves: The petioles of the leaves are usually longer than the blades, which are hastate, or spear-shaped and toothed or cleft below the middle.

Use or Importance: The Arrow-leaved Violet, like most other violets, is noted as a species whose importance is mainly its presence and charm as a small, early blooming plant of somewhat delicate nature.

Habitat: Arrow-leaved Violet is a characterisitic plant of sandy prairies, although it is not restricted to that habitat. It may also be found in moist habitats.

Range: The range of this species is from New England to Minnesota, south to Texas and Georgia.

BLUE VIOLET
(*Viola sororia* Willd.)

Season and Stature: This common Blue Violet is an early or cool-season native plant. It blooms during the Spring aspect. It attains a height of about 10 cm or more.

Flowers: The flowers are deep blue with a whitish center.

Leaves: The leaves are reniform, or ovate, cordate or abruptly pointed and smooth or hairy.

Use or Importance: Violets are small plants having little importance other than their presence and beauty. Violets are reported to have both edible flowers and leaves. The leaves are reported to be rich in vitamins A and C. Both leaves and flowers are mixed with other pot herbs. Tea from the leaves is, according to folk reports, supposed to strengthen the heart and induce sleep.

Habitat: Blue Violet, which is the state flower of Illinois, grows in woodlands, prairies, and in lawns.

Range: This species ranges from Quebec to eastern North Dakota, south to eastern Texas and central Florida.

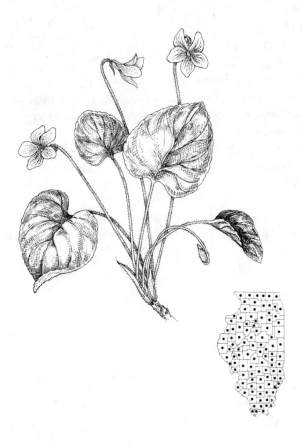

SIX-WEEKS FESCUE
(*Vulpia octoflora* (Walt.) Rydb.)

Season and Stature: The prairie grass flora is made up of few annual species. Six-weeks Fescue is one of them, and is a member of what is referred to as the minor grasses. It is a native species which grows and flowers during the cool-season, or during the early Summer. It forms tufts and grows to a height of about 15 cm. Its name is taken from its period of growth. It passes from seed germination to maturity in approximately six weeks.

Flowers: The narrow panicle has four to ten spikelets, and several florets per spikelet. The entire plant turns brown or straw-colored at maturity and becomes easily recognized.

Leaves: This species is a slender annual with erect, narrow leaves.

Use or Importance: The Six-weeks Fescue is of little importance other than to provide some small amount of cover where none may have existed before.

Habitat: This small plant grows on a variety of soils and is usually to be found where the existing sward has been thinned to a very open condition by overgrazing or other disturbance. It is an invading species in degenerating prairies.

Range: Six-weeks Fescue is widely spread throughout the United States. The life cycle of the plant allows it to fit into most any climatic circumstance in the United States.

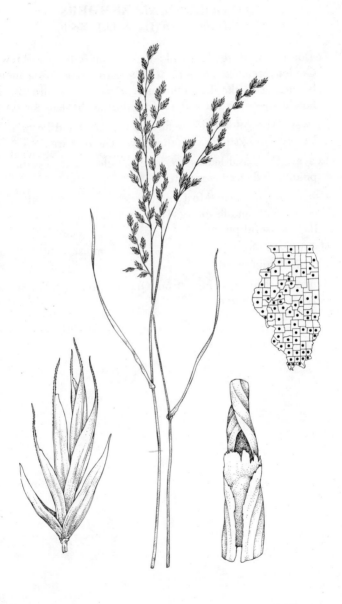

GOLDEN ALEXANDERS
(*Zizia aurea* (L.) W.D.J. Koch)

Season and Stature: The Golden Alexanders is also known as the Golden Meadow Parsnip. It is a native, cool-season perennial belonging to the Umbelliferae, or parsley family. It attains a height up to 75 cm and blooms during the late Spring aspect.

Flowers: The golden yellow flowers are small and borne in umbels having 9 to 25 short, ascending rays. The rays are up to 5 cm long.

Leaves: The basal leaves are long petioled, 2 to 3 ternately compound, and sharply serrate.

Use or Importance: Most members of the Umbelliferae supply condiments and flavoring. This species, however, is not known to have a useful purpose.

Habitat: Golden Alexanders occurs in moist habitats, including prairies and woods.

Range: This species ranges from Quebec to Saskatchewan, south to Texas and Georgia.

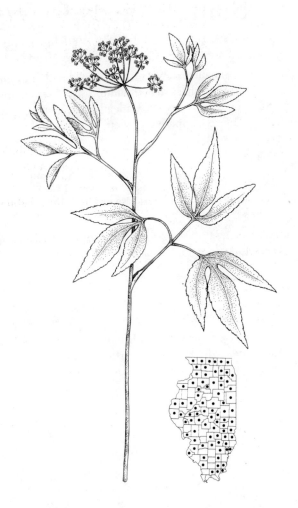

Some Places to Visit Prairies in Illinois

Several remnant patches of prairie still may be found in Illinois. Some of these prairies are sizeable, others are exceedingly small. The State of Illinois has been a leader in the preservation of native prairies. The accompanying map (Fig. 3) indicates by number where some of these prairies may be found. Those prairies which are mapped are:

1	Ayers Sand Prairie	109 acres	Illinois Department of Conservation
2	Beach Cemetery Prairie	2.5 acres	Natural Land Institute
3	Goose Lake Prairie	1513 acres	Illinois Department of Conservation
4	Weston Cemetery Prairie	5 acres	Town of Yates
5	Mississippi River Sand Hills	45 acres	Illinois Department of Conservation
6	Henry Allan Gleason	110 acres	Illinois Department of Conservation
7	Jasper County Prairie Chicken Sanctuary	407 acres	Illinois Department of Conservation
8	Marion County Prairie Chicken Sanctuary	160 acres	Illinois Department of Conservation
9	Fults Hill Prairie	373 acres	Illinois Department of Conservation

For a more extensive list of Illinois prairies, the interested person should write to the Illinois Department of Conservation, Division of Forestry, R #5, Springfield, Illinois 62707.

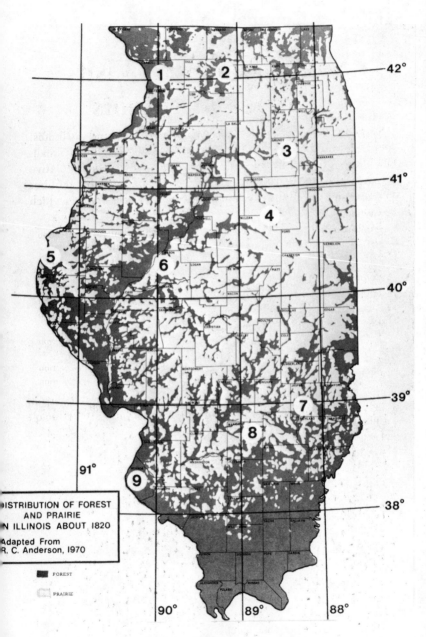

DISTRIBUTION OF FOREST
AND PRAIRIE
IN ILLINOIS ABOUT 1820

Adapted From
R. C. Anderson, 1970

■ FOREST

PRAIRIE

FIGURE 3

Index to Common and Scientific Names